The Problem Solver™

Activities for Learning Problem-Solving Strategies

Teacher Resource Book
Second Edition

Grade
1

Judy Goodnow
Shirley Hoogeboom

Wright Group

The McGraw-Hill Companies

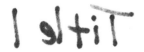

Acknowledgments

The authors wish to thank Heather McDonald for the problems she contributed to this book.

Judy Goodnow has authored and coauthored over 100 books and software programs for mathematics and problem solving. She has taught children from kindergarten through sixth grade. She holds a bachelor of arts degree from Wellesley College, a master's degree from Stanford University, and a California Teaching Credential from San Jose State University.

Shirley Hoogeboom has authored and coauthored over 100 books for mathematics and language arts. She has been a classroom teacher, and has conducted workshops for teachers on problem solving and on using math manipulatives. She holds a bachelor of arts degree in Education from Calvin College, where she earned a Michigan Teaching Credential. She completed further studies at California State University, Hayward, where she earned a California Teaching Credential.

www.WrightGroup.com

Send all inquiries to:
Wright Group/McGraw-Hill
P.O. Box 812960
Chicago, Illinois 60681

ISBN 978-0-07-704103-8
MHID 0-07-704103-8

2 3 4 5 6 7 8 9 MAL 13 12 11 10 09 08

The *McGraw·Hill* Companies

Contents

About *The Problem Solver*

What's new about this revised program?

For years, teachers have been using *The Problem Solver* to teach their students an organized approach to problem solving using ten strategies. In this revised program, we have retained this approach and have added features that reflect the increased emphasis on algebraic thinking, data analysis and graphing, geometry, and measurement in the math curriculum, and also greater emphasis on student writing.

In the Teacher Resource Book, we have added new Teaching Problems and included an Extension Problem, with solution, for each Teaching Problem. We have also added new Practice Problems, which provides you with a richer collection of reproducible problems, and we have revised all Teaching and Practice Problems for greater clarity and to include more up-to-date situations. Each Teaching Plan is now laid out on two pages, each laid out to match the corresponding page in the Student Workbook. Charts showing information about the math skills and the strategies used in each problem have been added. Using these charts will make it easier than ever for you to coordinate problem solving with your daily mathematics program. We have also included a section on assessment, with rubrics and ideas for assessing each student's progress in problem solving.

The Teacher Resource CD, provided along with the Teacher Resource Book, is also new to the program. It includes the Practice Problems that appear as mini reference versions in the Teacher Resource Book. The CD also includes English and Spanish Recording Sheets for students to use to organize and record their work, and a set of examples of student work that serve as models to help you assess students' solutions.

In the new Student Workbooks, each Teaching Problem is laid out on two pages, with increased space for the students to record their work and their thinking. Student Workbooks are easy to use and allow students to keep a record of their work that they can refer to as they solve other problems.

The Student Workbook is now available in English and in Spanish. The Teacher Resource Book includes examples of students' answers in both languages, as well as the Spanish translation of Extension Problems and the discussion of the strategy. Spanish and English versions of the Practice Problems can be printed from the Teacher Resource CD.

How do these materials teach problem solving?

The Problem Solver guides students step-by-step through instruction in mathematical problem solving. With these materials you teach students the easy-to-learn Four-Step Method of problem solving (explained on page xii). You also model the use of ten basic problem-solving strategies (described on pages xiii–xvii) that are useful at every grade level. The goal is to help students become competent, confident, and creative problem solvers. You can use *The Problem Solver* as an introduction to problem solving, as a review of the problem-solving process and strategies, or as a means of enriching students' experience with solving nonroutine problems.

Does this program support NCTM Standards?

The standards articulated by the National Council of Teachers of Mathematics (NCTM) were a guiding force in this revision of *The Problem Solver*. In its *Principles and Standards for School Mathematics*, NCTM emphasizes the importance of problem solving for all students from Pre-Kindergarten through the twelfth grade. The problem-solving standard specifies four key goals for instructional programs: that they "enable all students to

- build new mathematical knowledge through problem solving;
- solve problems that arise in mathematics and in other contexts;
- apply and adapt a variety of appropriate strategies to solve problems;
- monitor and reflect on the process of mathematics problem solving." (NCTM 2000, 52)

The problems in this program involve all five content areas of the mathematics curriculum: Number and Operations, Algebra, Geometry, Measurement, and Data Analysis and Probability. *The Problem Solver* also incorporates the five process standards identified by NCTM: Problem Solving, Reasoning and Proof, Communication, Connections, and Representation.

As students work on the problems, they learn to reason and to communicate in many different ways. They represent their work by writing, drawing pictures or diagrams, using objects, and making tables and charts. Students make connections among content areas as well as between mathematics and real-life situations.

How is this program organized?

This revised edition of *The Problem Solver* includes a Teacher Resource Book and Student Workbooks for each grade from 1 through 5, and for the middle school grades 6–8 combined.

The Teacher Resource Book begins with a series of Teaching Problems that you use to introduce the four-step method of problem solving and the ten solution strategies. The Teaching Problems are carefully sequenced by level of difficulty. They are presented in groups of three, giving students an opportunity to use the same strategy three times on similarly structured problems. The Student Workbook parallels this lesson sequence, presenting all Teaching Problems on two-page layouts.

Following the Teaching Problems is a bank of reproducible Practice Problems that offer additional opportunities for students to apply their problem-solving skills. Unlike the Teaching Problems, which have students use a suggested strategy, the Practice Problems make no suggestions as to which strategy could be used. This allows students to choose the strategy, or combination of strategies, that they believe will be most helpful.

How can I link the materials with my math curriculum?

If you intend to coordinate the material in *The Problem Solver* with the lessons in your math textbook, the charts on the following pages can facilitate your planning. In particular, the chart of Math Content Strands and Skills highlights the specific mathematics skills students use to solve each problem. To select the problems that best coordinate with your textbook units, you can scan the chart to find problems that involve the mathematics your students are currently studying.

Overview of Strategies and Skills in *The Problem Solver*, Grade 1

TEN PROBLEM–SOLVING STRATEGIES	Use or Make a Table	Make an Organized List	Act Out or Use Objects	Use or Look for a Pattern	Use or Make a Picture or Diagram	Guess and Check	Work Backwards	Use Logical Reasoning	Make It Simpler	Brainstorm
1								■		
2								■		
3								■		
4		■								
5		■								
6		■								
7	■									
8	■									
9	■									
10								■		
11								■		
12								■		
13					■					
14					■					
15					■					
16		■								
17		■								
18		■								
19						■				
20						■				
21						■				
22					■					
23					■					
24					■					
25			■							
26			■							
27			■							
28	■									
29	■									
30	■									
31					■					
32					■					
33					■					
34			■							
35			■							
36			■							
37	■									
38	■									
39	■									
40					■					

TEACHING PROBLEMS

TEN PROBLEM-SOLVING STRATEGIES

	Use or Make a Table	Make an Organized List	Act Out or Use Objects	Use or Look for a Pattern	Use or Make a Picture or Diagram	Guess and Check	Work Backwards	Use Logical Reasoning	Make It Simpler	Brainstorm
TEACHING PROBLEMS										
41				▨						
42				▨						
43							▨			
44							▨			
45							▨			
46					▨					
47					▨					
48					▨					
49									▨	
50									▨	
51									▨	
52										▨
53										▨
54										▨
55					▨					
56					▨					
57					▨					
58					▨					
PRACTICE PROBLEMS										
59								▨		
60		▨								
61	▨									
62								▨		
63					▨					
64		▨								
65						▨				
66				▨						
67			▨							
68	▨									
69				▨						
70			▨							
71	▨									
72				▨						
73							▨			
74					▨					
75									▨	
76										▨
77					▨					
78					▨					
79	▨									
80		▨								
81						▨				
82			▨							

The strategies indicated here for the Practice Problems (59–82) are those which were used for solving similar Teaching Problems. However, the students' choices of strategy may vary.

MATH CONTENT STRANDS AND SKILL FOCUS		Number and Operations	Algebra	Geometry	Measurement	Data Analysis and Probability	Skill Focus
TEACHING PROBLEMS	41	●	●				Identify number pattern; count by 3s
	42	●	●				Identify number pattern; count back by 2s
	43	●					Compare numbers (more than); add
	44	●					Compare numbers (more than); add
	45	●					Compare numbers (more than); add
	46	●		●			Find all the paths between two places on a map (picture)
	47	●		●			Find all the paths between two places on a map (picture)
	48	●		●			Find all the paths between two places on a map (picture)
	49	●					Find out how many pairs could be made among 4 people
	50	●					Find out how many pairs could be made among 4 people
	51	●					Find out how many pairs could be made among 5 people
	52			●			Use spatial visualization to solve a puzzle
	53			●			Use spatial visualization to solve a puzzle
	54	●		●			Use spatial visualization and identify order (behind, in front of, between) to solve a puzzle
	55	●				●	Read picture graph; compare amounts (more than, equal)
	56	●				●	Read bar graph; compare amounts (more than, fewer than)
	57	●				●	Read bar graph; compare amounts (more than); odd numbers
	58	●			●	●	Read bar graph; compare lengths (longer than, same length)
PRACTICE PROBLEMS	59					●	Analyze data; identify characteristics
	60	●					Find all ways to combine items from two sets
	61	●				●	Use clues to identify a mystery number; compare numbers
	62	●				●	Analyze data; identify size (largest) and other characteristics
	63	●					Use a number line (picture map); count forward and backward
	64	●					Find combinations of two numbers that sum to 7
	65	●			●		Find combinations of three numbers that sum to 10 dollars
	66		●				Identify and extend a visual pattern (AABC)
	67	●				●	Analyze data; identify order (first, in front of, behind)
	68	●	●				Identify and use patterns; count on by 3s; use ratio of 1 to 3
	69	●	●				Use and extend a number pattern; count on from 1 by 3s
	70	●					Identify part/whole; add; subtract; arrange numbers as in a Venn diagram
	71	●	●		●		Use and extend a number pattern; count on from 5¢ by 2s
	72	●	●				Identify a number pattern; count on from 8 by 2s
	73	●					Compare numbers (oldest, older than, youngest); add; subtract
	74	●		●			Find all the paths between two places on a map (picture)
	75	●		●			Find the total number of lines if each dot is connected to every other dot with a line
	76			●			Use spatial visualization to solve a puzzle
	77	●				●	Read bar graph; compare amounts (equal numbers, half as many)
	78	●			●	●	Read bar graph; compare temperatures (warmer, cooler); count by 5s
	79	●				●	Use clues to identify a mystery number; compare numbers
	80	●					Find combinations of two numbers that sum to 11
	81	●					Find combinations of three amounts that sum to 18
	82	●	●				Identify part/whole; add; subtract; arrange numbers as in a Venn diagram

Teaching Suggestions

How should I present the lessons?

Lessons in *The Problem Solver* follow an easy-to-use format, with a two-page lesson plan for each Teaching Problem. We recommend that you present the problems in the order they appear. The problems have been carefully sequenced so that they progress from easy to more challenging. The math skills required to solve even the most challenging problems are those which students usually have mastered by the middle of first grade.

The lesson plans offer a script to help you guide students through the problem-solving process, modeling the Four-Step Method and showing why a particular strategy is useful. The script includes questions you can ask and shows sample student responses in italics, in English and in Spanish. You will want to add further questions of your own as you hear how your students are responding. You can present the lessons to the entire class or to small groups. Some teachers like to use an overhead projector or a computer for presentations.

Before starting on the Teaching Problems, you may want to introduce separately the Four-Step Method that students will be using throughout the program. For a discussion of this method, see page xii.

How should I use the Student Workbooks?

Have the students work in their Student Workbooks while you present each lesson. To start the lesson, first read the problem aloud to the group; then have students read it again. As you guide them through the problem-solving process, give students time to record their work and make notes about their thinking. In this way, the Student Workbook becomes a valuable problem-solving reference that students can use as they work on the Practice Problems and any other problem-solving activities.

What if my students have different ways to solve the problems?

Students will likely offer a wide range of responses to the step-by-step questions. There are often many different ways to approach a given problem, and you should encourage students to share their thoughts. As NCTM has stated:

> Sharing gives students opportunities to hear new ideas and compare them with their own and to justify their thinking. As students struggle with problems, seeing a variety of successful solutions improves their chance of learning useful strategies and allows them to determine if some strategies are more flexible and efficient [than others]. (NCTM 2000, 118)

The students will have even more freedom to think through their own approaches when they work on the Practice Problems.

Each problem introduces and focuses on one strategy. Students may use more than one strategy, however, to solve a problem. You may want to discuss this with them, and you may want to encourage them to identify all the strategies they are using; or you may prefer to stay focused on just one strategy.

How do the Practice Problems fit into the program?

Each lesson plan identifies one or two Practice Problems that are similar to the Teaching Problem students have just solved. You can reproduce any or all of these from the CD in the Teacher Resource Book for follow-up work. Keep in mind, however, that no particular strategies are indicated on the Practice Problem page. This gives students the opportunity to analyze the problem themselves and choose the strategy that they believe will be most helpful for solving it.

Teaching Suggestions continued

The Recording Sheet provided in the Student Workbook and on the Teacher Resource CD gives students an outline of the Four-Step Method: FIND OUT, CHOOSE A STRATEGY, SOLVE IT, and LOOK BACK. However, presenting some problems with no such guidance gives students a chance to call up all their problem-solving skills—much as they will have to do in textbooks, on tests, and in daily life. Students can use the Thinking Questions at the end of the Student Workbook as prompts while they analyze, choose a strategy, and find solutions. You could also make a large poster of the Thinking Questions for classroom reference. After students complete a problem, they can respond to one or more of the Writing Questions (page xx) to reflect on their solution process.

- The Talk About It section after each Extension Problem suggests a question you can use to enhance students' discussion of their solution strategies.
- Having students write a problem that is similar to the one they just solved increases their understanding of problem-solving situations and solution methods. Students can exchange their problems for more practice, and you might consider adding some of the problems your students create to the bank of Practice Problems.
- Some teachers like to give students one or more of the Writing Questions (page xx), asking them to tell how they solved the problem and to explain their thinking process in writing. These questions can also be used with the Practice Problems as a tool for assessment, as described on page xviii.

What else is suggested for lesson follow-up?

Several additional follow-up options are built into *The Problem Solver.*

- Extension Problems offer further work that is related to the Teaching Problem. Students solve these problems independently, then meet with a partner or in small groups to discuss their solution methods. This encourages them to share their different ways of thinking about and solving the problem.

The Four-Step Method

The Four-Step Method is a systematic approach to problem solving that can be used for solving any problem. You may want to discuss these steps with your students before beginning work with the Teaching Problems. Understanding the purpose of each step can help students experience greater success.

Step 1 • FIND OUT

The first step for students in solving a problem is to make sure they know what the problem is about and what they are being asked to find. Encourage them to try explaining the problem in their own words; this helps them better understand the information. They should ask themselves:

- What is happening in the problem?
- What do I have to find out to solve the problem?
- Are there any words or ideas I don't understand?
- What information can I use?
- Am I missing any information that I need?

Step 2 • CHOOSE A STRATEGY

After students have identified what they are looking for and they know what information they have, they can make a plan for solving the problem. Now is the time to choose the strategy or combination of strategies that they think will be most helpful. They will find that there is often more than one way to solve the problem. In some cases, the problem may have to be broken down into smaller problems before the larger problem can be solved.

Step 3 • SOLVE IT

Students now use the strategy they have chosen to solve the problem. It is very important that they record their work in a way that lets them see what they have completed. It is possible they will discover that the strategy they chose is not as helpful as they thought it would be. Emphasize that they should not be discouraged, but rather choose a different strategy and try again.

Step 4 • LOOK BACK

After students have solved the problem, they should always check their answers by reading the problem again, looking back over each step, and checking their calculations. They should ask themselves:

- Did I answer the question asked in the problem?
- Is more than one answer possible?
- Is my math correct?
- Does my answer make sense? Is it reasonable?
- Can I explain why I think my answer is correct?

Ten Problem-Solving Strategies

Act Out or Use Objects

Some students may find it helpful to act out a problem or to move objects around while they are trying to solve a problem. It allows them to develop mental images of the data in the problem and the steps they must take to solve it. The objects need not be elaborate: common manipulatives such as cubes, play money, pattern blocks, chips, colored counters, and even small scraps of paper will usually work well to represent numbers and colors. Using this strategy is especially helpful for visualizing arrangements, combinations, and relationships in the elements of a problem. In the following problem, for example, students can use labeled scraps of paper to represent the different colors of fish. They can move the papers around on the line of fish until all the conditions are met.

Problem 25: Four fish line up to swim through the castle in their fish tank. The red fish is first in line. The blue fish is in front of the yellow fish. The green fish is in front of the blue fish. What color is the last fish in the line?

Solution: Yellow

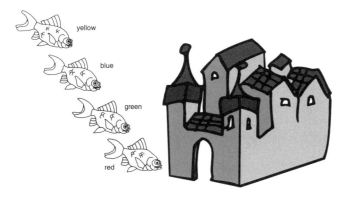

Use or Make a Picture or Diagram

Some problems give a picture, diagram, or map as part of the data. For other problems, students may find it helpful to draw their own pictures or diagrams. The pictures or diagrams need not be well drawn. It is most important that they help the problem solver understand and manipulate the data in a problem. Using diagrams is almost a necessity for some problems, particularly those which involve mapping. In the following example, students are given a map on which to trace a path. For example:

Problem 13: Susan is going to school. She has to cross 8 bridges on her way. She starts out from her house and crosses 6 bridges. Stop! She dropped her lunch somewhere. Susan turns around and goes back across 2 bridges. She finds her lunch. She turns around again and goes across 4 bridges. Where is Susan now?

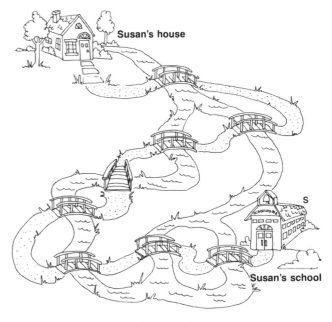

Solution: Susan is at the school.

Use or Make a Table

In some problems, students may need to use data from a table or a chart. In other problems, they may need to keep track of data in an orderly way. Making their own tables by listing key numbers in sequence can help students find missing data and discover or extend number patterns. This strategy is often used in combination with other strategies. In the example below, the table is used to keep track of data and could also be used for identifying a number pattern.

Problem 28: Rose and Rocky Raccoon are going to have a party. They wrote notes to their friends to ask them to come. Rocky wrote faster than Rose did. In the time it took Rose to write 1 note, Rocky wrote 3 notes. Rocky and Rose kept writing in the same way until they finished all the notes. Then Rose put stamps on the 4 notes she wrote. How many notes did Rocky write?

Solution: 12 notes

Number of Notes Rose Wrote	1	2	3	4
Number of Notes Rocky Wrote	□□□ 3	□□□ □□□ 6	□□□ □□□ □□□ 9	□□□ □□□ □□□ □□□ 12

Make an Organized List

Making an organized list helps problem solvers organize their thinking about a problem. An organized list is a systematic way of recording a series of computations or combinations of items. An organized list makes it easy to review what has been done and to identify important steps that still need to be completed. It is especially helpful when a student wants to consider all the possibilities in order to find those that fit the problem. For example:

Problem 4: Katie Kangaroo is going to school! She takes out her sneakers and socks. Katie has a pair of red sneakers and a pair of yellow sneakers. She has one pair of blue socks and one pair of green socks. What are the different sets of sneakers and socks that Katie can put on today?

Solution:

1. red sneakers and blue socks

2. red sneakers and green socks

3. yellow sneakers and blue socks

4. yellow sneakers and green socks

Guess and Check

Guessing and checking is helpful when a problem asks for one solution but not all possible solutions to a problem. When problem solvers use this strategy, they guess the answer and then check to see if it fits with the other data given in the problem. If it does not, they decide whether the guess was too high or too low; then they try to come closer with their next guess. They keep guessing and checking until they find a correct answer. For example:

Problem 19: Juan looked at the toys in Skip's Junk Shop. Skip is selling some little green turtles, rubber birds, squeaky bears, wooden dogs, and fuzzy cats. Juan bought 3 different toys. He paid 12 cents in all. Which 3 toys did Juan buy?

turtle	bird	bear	dog	cat
3 cents	4 cents	8 cents	9 cents	1 cent

Guess 1:   3¢ + 4¢ + 8¢ = 15¢
           Too high

Guess 2:   3¢ + 4¢ + 1¢ = 8¢
           Too low

Guess 3:   3¢ + 8¢ + 1¢ = 12¢

Solution: Turtle, bear, cat

Use or Look for a Pattern

Looking for patterns is a very important strategy for problem solving. A pattern occurs when a relationship is repeated again and again. A pattern may be numerical, visual, or behavioral. Identifying a pattern enables students to predict what will "come next" and what will happen again and again in the same way. In some problems, a pattern is given and students use it to solve the problem. In other problems, students must identify and extend the pattern in order to find a solution. Making a table often reveals patterns in data, so these two strategies are frequently used in combination. For example:

Problem 40: Simon Squirrel's cousins are coming to visit him next week. He has been getting food ready for their visit. On Monday he cracked 1 nut. On Tuesday he cracked 3 nuts. On Wednesday he cracked 5 nuts, and on Thursday he cracked 7 nuts. Simon is following a number pattern, so he knows how many nuts he will crack on Friday. How many nuts will he crack on Friday?

Solution: 9 nuts

Monday	Tuesday	Wednesday	Thursday	Friday
⬜	⬜	⬜	⬜	⬜
1	⬜	⬜	⬜	⬜
	⬜	⬜	⬜	⬜
	3	⬜	⬜	⬜
		⬜	⬜	⬜
		5	⬜	⬜
			⬜	⬜
			7	⬜
				⬜
				9

Work Backwards

To solve certain problems, the problem solver must make a series of computations, starting with data presented at the end of the problem and ending with data presented at the beginning of the problem. For example:

Problem 43: Herman and Polly say Frank catches the most fish because he has the best worms. Maybe they are right. Frank Fox does catch fish! Today he caught 5 more fish than Polly caught. Polly Pig pulled up 4 more fish than Herman did. Herman Rabbit caught only 2 fish. How many fish did Frank catch?

Solution: 11 fish

Herman	Polly	Frank
2	6	11

Use Logical Reasoning

Logical reasoning is really used for all problem solving. However, there are types of problems that include or imply various conditional statements such as: "If something is true, then ..." or "If something is not true, then ...". This kind of problem requires formal logical reasoning as the problem solver works through the statements given in the problem. In the following problem, for example, students will use statements such as: "If Ryan's favorite animal has 4 legs, then the owl can't be his favorite animal."

Problem 1: On Ryan's farm there is a rooster, a cat, a rabbit, a dog, and an owl. Ryan likes all the animals, but he likes one best of all.

• It has 4 legs.
• It has ears that stand straight up.
• It has a short tail.

Which animal does Ryan like best?

Solution:

Make It Simpler

Sometimes a problem can be made simpler by reducing large numbers to small numbers, or by reducing the number of items given in a problem. Having a simpler representation can make it easier to recognize the operation or process that can be used to solve the more complex problem. The simpler representation may even reveal a pattern that can be used to solve the problem. In the following example, students can act out or draw diagrams of solutions to simpler problems with two and three swimmers, and then record the pattern the solutions to the simpler problems reveal. For example:

Problem 49: Ann, Betsy, Carol, and Dee are taking swimming lessons at the park. They are getting ready to give a show. One part of the show is very pretty. The girls hold colored ribbons and float in the water. Each girl is joined to each of the other girls by a ribbon. How many ribbons do the girls need?

How many ribbons do the girls need if

2 swimmers are swimming in the show? _____1_____

3 swimmers are swimming in the show? _____3_____

4 swimmers are swimming in the show? _____6_____

Solution: 6 ribbons

Brainstorm

This strategy is often used when all else fails. When students cannot think of a similar problem they have solved before and cannot think of another strategy to use, brainstorming is a good strategy to try. It leads students to look at a problem in new and unusual ways. Encourage students to open up their minds, allow for inspiration, be creative, be flexible, and keep on trying until a light goes on! For example:

Problem 52: Fiona is giving you a puzzle to solve. She says, "There are 2 circles on the floor. One circle is large. The other circle is small. There are 3 lions in the large circle. There are 2 lions in the small circle. But there are only 3 lions in all. Where is the small circle, and where are the lions?"

Solution:

Assessment

Before starting to use *The Problem Solver* with your students, you can assess their knowledge of the problem-solving process by giving them Practice Problems that involve different strategies. You could choose problems either from students' previous grade level or from their present level. Assessing their abilities to solve these test problems will help you decide which problems to use with your students. Such a pretest will also give you a baseline for evaluating student progress if you repeat this procedure at the end of the year.

As they learn the problem-solving process, students need to understand that the formulation of a plan and the execution of that plan are as vital as finding the correct answer. There are various ways to assess students' abilities in these areas.

- Have students use the Recording Sheet to organize and record their work.

- Observe students as they solve problems alone or with a partner or small group. You will gain meaningful insights into their abilities to select and use appropriate techniques and their understanding of mathematical concepts. You will also be able to assess their abilities to articulate, to listen, to be flexible, and to rethink.

- Have students write an answer to one or more of the Writing Questions (page xx) after they solve a Practice Problem. You might duplicate the Writing Questions on the back of a Practice Problem and indicate which ones you would like the students to write about.

- Challenge students to write a problem similar to one they have completed. The problems students write will indicate how well students understand a type of problem and the process for solving this kind of problem.

- Collect students' work on the Practice Problems and use one of the following rubrics to evaluate what they have done. These assessment tools help you evaluate the quality of students' work as a whole, not just the correctness of their answers.

When using the 4-Point Rubric or the Analytic Rubric, you may want to modify the scoring system. It may make sense to give a 2.5, $3\frac{1}{2}$, 1+, 2−, and so on. Use whatever scoring system works for you and your students.

If you use the Analytic Rubric, be sure to have the students respond to the Writing Questions. You will need this information to adequately assess the Look Back section. You can also obtain this feedback from informal interviews. Again, use the method that works best for you.

If students are just beginning problem solving, then the type of feedback the Analytic Rubric provides might be useful for the students. In this way they can see where they need improvement.

Whatever approach you take, make sure that students understand how their work is being assessed and involve them in the assessment process. Share your assessment form with them so they know what is expected. On at least some occasions, have students assess themselves. For this purpose, you might simplify your rubric, or have students use a simple 1–5 rating scale such as this:

1 – I don't know what to do.
2 – I'm beginning to understand.
3 – I'm doing OK, but I'm not sure about every step.
4 – I get it, and I'm sure my answer is right.
5 – I get it, and I gave a great explanation!

Performance samples to help you use the 4-Point Rubric and the Analytic Rubric are on the Teacher Resource CD. The performance samples are just guides. They may vary widely from your students' work, depending on the time of year and your students' prior problem-solving experience.

4-Point Rubric

You could use this rubric to evaluate a student's work on the problem as a whole, using one overall score from 1 to 4.

1: Poor
- Uses inappropriate strategies
- Makes major errors
- Shows inadequate explanation of thinking
- Presents incorrect solution

2: Fair
- Gives adequate response
- Makes some errors
- Gives incoherent or unclear explanation
- Shows partial understanding of mathematical ideas
- May use appropriate strategy
- Shows some parts of solution process
- May have incorrect solution

3: Good
- Uses strategy or strategies appropriately
- Gives complete response
- Gives good, clear explanation of thinking
- Shows understanding of mathematical concepts
- Shows solution process, including appropriate graphs, diagrams, and so on
- Presents correct solution

4: Outstanding
- Same as Good plus the following:
- Shows original and creative thinking
- Gives strong explanation of reasoning
- May use multiple strategies or multiple approaches
- Demonstrates outstanding grasp of mathematical ideas
- Exceeds expectations

Analytic Rubric

With this rubric, you could evaluate each part of the problem-solving process separately, with points scored for each part as shown.

Understands problem
0 Shows no understanding
1 Shows partial understanding
2 Shows full understanding, extracts relevant information, and understands question

Chooses strategies
0 Chooses inappropriate strategies or no strategies
1 Chooses appropriate strategies, but does not use them effectively
2 Chooses one or more appropriate strategies and uses them effectively

Solves the problem
0 Does not formulate a plan
1 Has a plan, but shows errors in thinking
2 Has a thoughtful plan and executes it well

Finds answer
0 Has no answer
1 Has an answer, but there are errors
2 Has correct answer

Looks back
0 Has inadequate or no explanation
1 Has explanation that is not clear, but demonstrates some understanding
2 Has explanation that shows clear understanding of mathematical ideas

Writing Questions

Name _____

Problem Number _____

Tell about or explain the problem in your own words.

What strategy did you choose? Why?

How did you solve the problem? Tell about your thinking.

Why does your answer make sense?

Thinking Questions
Questions to think about as you are solving problems

FIND OUT

What is the problem about?

What question do I have to answer?

What do I have to find out to solve the problem?

Are there any words or ideas I don't understand?

What information can I use?

Am I missing any information that I need?

CHOOSE A STRATEGY

Have I solved a problem like this before?

What strategy helped me solve it?

Can I use the same strategy for this problem?

SOLVE IT

What information should I start with?

Do I need to add or subtract?

How can I organize the information that I use or find?

Is the strategy I chose helpful?

Would another strategy be better?

Do I need to use more than one strategy?

Is my work easy to read and understand? Is it complete?

LOOK BACK

Did I answer the question that was asked in the problem?

Is more than one answer possible?

Is my math correct?

Does my answer make sense?

Can I explain why I think my answer is correct?

Use Logical Reasoning
Usar la lógica

1

On Ryan's farm there is a rooster, a cat, a rabbit, a dog, and an owl. Ryan likes all the animals, but he likes one best of all.

• It has 4 legs.

• It has ears that stand straight up.

• It has a short tail.

Which animal does Ryan like best?

1 FIND OUT

A. **What question do you have to answer to solve the problem?** *Which animal does Ryan like best?* ● *¿Cuál es el animal que más le gusta a Ryan?*

B. **What animals are on Ryan's farm?** *A rooster, a cat, a dog, a rabbit, and an owl* ● *Un gallo, un gato, un perro, un conejo y un búho*

C. **Does Ryan like all the animals the same?** *No, he likes one animal the best.* ● *No, a él le gusta uno de los aminales más que los demas.*

D. **What do you know about the animal that Ryan likes best?** *It has 4 legs, ears that stand straight up, and a short tail.* ● *Tiene 4 patas, orejas largas que se le paran hacia atrás y una cola corta.*

2 CHOOSE A STRATEGY

Does the problem show you exactly which animal Ryan likes best? *No* Does it give you some clues or hints about the animal Ryan likes best? *Yes*

The little picture at the top of your paper means that we can use a special kind of thinking to solve this problem. It is called logical reasoning. We'll read each clue and look at the pictures. If any animal does not fit the clue, then we'll cross it out.

● ¿Les dice el problema cuál es el animal que más le gusta a Ryan? *No* ¿Les da pistas acerca del animal que más le gusta a Ryan? *Sí*

El dibujito en la parte de arriba de la página significa que pueden usar un razonamiento especial para resolver este problema. Ese razonamiento se llama usar la lógica. Leeremos las pistas y observaremos los dibujos. Si hay un animal que no coincide con las pistas, entonces lo tachamos.

TEACHING TIP

Introduce the language of logical thinking by using conditional, or "If...then" statements: **IF I'm thinking of a 4-legged animal, THEN a cat could be my animal. IF I'm thinking of a 4-legged animal, THEN a chicken is not my animal.** ● **SI estoy pensando en un animal de cuatro patas, ENTONCES un gato puede ser ese animal. SI estoy pensando en un animal de cuatro patas, ENTONCES ese animal no puede ser una gallina.**

③ SOLVE IT

Look at the animal pictures on your paper.

A. **Let's read the clues one at a time to solve the mystery. The first clue is: It has 4 legs. Which animal could it be? The rooster?** *No* **Why?** *It has 2 legs.* ● *Tiene 2 patas.* **Cross out the rooster. Could it be the dog?** *Yes* ● *Sí* **Why?** *It has 4 legs.* ● *Tiene 4 patas.* **Could it be the cat?** *Yes* ● *Sí* **Could it be the owl?** *No* **Cross out the owl. Could it be the rabbit?** *Yes* ● *Sí*

B. **Let's use the second clue: It has ears that stand straight up. The rooster and the owl are already crossed out. Does the dog have ears that stand straight up?** *No* **Cross out the dog. Does the cat have ears that stand straight up?** *Yes* ● *Sí* **Does the rabbit have ears that stand straight up?** *Yes* ● *Sí*

C. **Let's use the third clue: It has a short tail. Does the cat have a short tail?** *No* **Cross out the cat. Does the rabbit have a short tail?** *Yes* ● *Sí* **Which animal does Ryan like best?**

Solution:

④ LOOK BACK

Let's look back at the problem to see if your answer fits with what the problem tells you and asks you to find. Listen to the problem again. Read the problem again. **Does your answer fit?**
● Verifica tu trabajo para saber si tu respuesta responde a lo que el problema plantea y te pide que hagas. Vuelve a escuchar el problema. ¿Es correcta tu respuesta?

EXTENSION PROBLEM

What would the answer be if the third clue told you that the animal had short ears? *The cat*

● **¿Qué contestarían si la tercera pista les dijera que los animales tienen orejas cortas?** *El gato*

TALK ABOUT IT

Ask questions like, **The cat wasn't the only animal with short ears. How did you know it was the cat?**
● **El gato no es el único animal que tiene orejas cortas. ¿Cómo supieron que era el gato?**

PRACTICE

Similar Practice Problem: 59

Use Logical Reasoning
Usar la lógica

2

Maricela and Jenna are playing a game called Guess My Shape.
Jenna draws some shapes and gives Maricela three clues about her
secret shape.

• It has more than three corners.

• All of its sides are the same length.

• It doesn't have square corners.

Which shape is Jenna's secret shape?

① FIND OUT

A. **What question do you have to answer to
solve the problem?** *Which shape is Jenna's
secret shape?* ● *¿Cuál es la figura secreta de
Jenna?*

B. **How many shapes did Jenna draw?** 6 **What
are the names of the shapes?** *Triangle,
square, circle, rectangle, hexagon, trapezoid*
● *Triángulo, cuadrado, círculo, rectángulo,
hexágono, trapezoide*

C. **What do you know about Jenna's secret
shape?** *It has more than 3 corners, all of its
sides are the same length, and it doesn't have
square corners.* ● *Tiene más de 3 esquinas,
todos sus lados son del mismo largo y no
tiene esquinas cuadradas.*

TEACHING TIP
Discuss the shapes Jenna drew and ways in which the shapes are alike and
different. Have the children find examples of square corners.

② CHOOSE A STRATEGY

**Does the problem show you exactly which
shape is Jenna's secret shape?** *No* **Does
it give you some clues or hints about the
shape?** *Yes*

The little picture at the top of your paper
means that you can use a special kind of
thinking to solve this problem. It is called
logical reasoning. We'll read each clue and
look at the pictures. If any shape does not
fit the clue, then we'll cross it out.

● ¿Les muestra el problema con exactitud
cuál es la forma de la figura secreta de
Jenna? *No* ¿Les da pistas para saber cuál
es la figura? *Sí*

El dibujito en la parte de arriba de la
página significa que pueden usar un
razonamiento especial para resolver este
problema. Ese razonamiento se llama
usar la lógica. Leeremos cada pista y
observaremos los dibujos. Si hay una
figura que no coincide con las pistas,
entonces la tachamos.

3 SOLVE IT

Look at the pictures of the shapes on your paper.

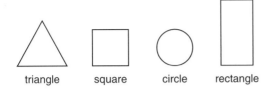

triangle   square   circle   rectangle

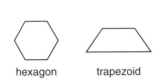

hexagon   trapezoid

A. **Let's use the first clue as you look at the picture: It has more than 3 corners. Which of the shapes fit this clue?** *The square, the rectangle, the hexagon, and the trapezoid* ● *El cuadrado, el rectángulo, el hexágono y el trapezoide* **If Jenna's shape has more than 3 corners, which shapes could *not* be Jenna's?** *The triangle and the circle* ● *El triángulo y el círculo* **Cross out the shapes that have 3 or fewer corners.**

B. **Let's use the second clue: All of its sides are the same length. Can it be the triangle?** *No, it has been crossed out already.* ● *No, ya ha sido tachado.* **Can it be the square?** *Yes* ● *Sí* **The rectangle?** *No, its sides are not all the same length.* ● *No, no todos sus lados tienen el mismo largo.* **Cross it out. The hexagon?** *Yes* ● *Sí* **The trapezoid?** *No* **Cross it out. Which shapes are not crossed out?** *The square and the hexagon* ● *El cuadrado y el hexágono*

C. **Let's use the third clue: It doesn't have square corners. Look at the shapes that are not crossed out. Does either of them have square corners?** *Yes, the square* ● *Sí, el cuadrado* **Can that be Jenna's shape?** *No, her shape doesn't have square corners.* ● *No, su figura no tiene esquinas cuadradas.* **Cross that shape out. Which shape is Jenna's secret shape?**

Solution:

hexagon

4 LOOK BACK

Let's look back at the problem to see if your answer fits with what the problem tells you and asks you to find. Listen to the problem again. Read the problem again. **Does your answer fit?**

EXTENSION PROBLEM

What would the answer be if the third clue told you that Jenna's secret shape has all square corners? *The square* ● **¿Qué contestarían si la tercera pista les dijera que la figura secreta de Jenna tiene todas las esquinas cuadradas?** *El cuadrado*

TALK ABOUT IT

Ask questions like, **How did you use the new clue to solve the problem?** ● **¿Cómo usaron la nueva pista para resolver el problema?**

PRACTICE

Similar Practice Problem: 59

Use Logical Reasoning
Usar la lógica

3

Dan and Delia are going to buy a toy. They both like one of the toys very much. Dan and Delia want to buy this toy.

- It has 4 wheels.
- It does not have a ladder.
- It has a back seat.

Which toy do Dan and Delia want to buy?

1 FIND OUT

A. **What question do you have to answer to solve the problem?** *Which toy do Dan and Delia want to buy?* ● *¿Cuál es el juguete que Dan y Delia quieren comprar?*

B. **How many toys are Dan and Delia looking at?** 5 **What are the toys?** *A race car, lumber truck, fire truck, van, and motorcycle* ● *Un carro de carreras, un camión, un camión de bomberos y una motocicleta de juguete*

C. **What do you know about the toy that Dan and Delia want to buy?** *It has 4 wheels. It does not have a ladder. It has a back seat.* ● *Tiene 4 ruedas. No tiene escalera. Tiene un asiento en la parte de atrás.*

TEACHING TIP
Help the children examine the toy vehicles by asking them to think of ways in which the vehicles are alike and different, such as the numbers of doors or wheels.

2 CHOOSE A STRATEGY

Does the problem tell you exactly which toy Dan and Delia want to buy? *No* **Does it give you some clues or hints about the toy?** *Yes*

What does the little picture at the top of your paper mean? *It means we can use a special kind of thinking to solve this problem.*
What else will help you solve the problem? *The clues and the picture*

● **¿Les dice el problema cuál es el juguete que Dan y Delia quieren comprar con exactitud?** *No* **¿Les da pistas para saber cuál es el juguete?** *Sí*

¿Qué significa el dibujito en la parte de arriba de la página? *Significa que podemos usar un razonamiento especial para resolver este problema.* **¿Qué más les puede ayudar a resolver el problema?** *Las pistas y los dibujos*

❸ SOLVE IT

Look at the pictures of toys on your paper.

A. **Let's use the first clue as you look at the picture: It has 4 wheels. Could it be the race car?** *Yes* ● *Sí* **Could it be the van?** *Yes* ● *Sí* **Could it be the fire truck?** *Yes* ● *Sí* **Could it be the lumber truck?** *No, because it has 8 wheels.* ● *No, porque tiene 8 ruedas* **Cross it out. Could it be the motorcycle?** *No, because it has only 2 wheels.* ● *No, porque tiene sólo 2 ruedas* **Cross out the motorcycle.**

B. **Let's use the second clue: It does not have a ladder. Could it be the race car?** *Yes* ● *Sí* **Could it be the van?** *Yes* ● *Sí* **Could it be the fire truck?** *No, because it has a ladder.* ● *No, porque tiene una escalera.* **Cross out the fire truck. How many toys are not crossed out?** *2*

C. **Let's use the third clue: It has a back seat. Look at the two toys that are not crossed out. Do both toys have back seats?** *No, the race car does not have a back seat.* ● *No, el carro de carreras no tiene un asiento en la parte de atrás.* **Which toy do Dan and Delia want to buy?**

Solution:

❹ LOOK BACK

Let's look back at the problem to see if your answer fits with what the problem tells you and asks you to find. Listen to the problem again. Read the problem again. **Does your answer fit?**

EXTENSION PROBLEM

What would the answer be if the third clue told you that the toy has no roof? *The race car*

● ¿Qué contestarían si la tercera pista les dijera que el juguete no tiene techo? *Que es el carro de carreras*

TALK ABOUT IT

Ask questions like, **Two of the toys had no roof. How did you know it was the race car?** ● **Dos de los juguetes no tenían techo. ¿Cómo supieron que era un carro de carreras?**

PRACTICE

Similar Practice Problem: 59

Make an Organized List
Hacer una lista

Content Strands:
Number and Operations Algebra

 Each child needs 4 crayons: red, yellow, blue, green.

4

Katie Kangaroo is going to school! She takes out her sneakers and socks. Katie has a pair of red sneakers and a pair of yellow sneakers. She has one pair of blue socks and one pair of green socks. What are the different sets of sneakers and socks that Katie can put on today?

1 FIND OUT

A. **What question do you have to answer to solve the problem?** *What are the different sets of sneakers and socks that Katie can put on today?* ● *¿Cuántas combinaciones de zapatos y calcetines se puede poner Katie hoy?*

B. **How many pairs of sneakers does Katie have?** *2* **What color is each pair?** *One is red and one is yellow.* ● *Un par es rojo y el otro es amarillo.*

C. **How many pairs of socks does Katie have?** *2* **What color is each pair?** *One is blue and one is green.* ● *Un par es azul y el otro es verde.*

D. **What does "pair" mean?** *Two of one kind* ● *Dos de la misma cosa*

E. **What is a set of sneakers and socks?** *One pair of sneakers and one pair of socks* ● *Un par de zapatos y un par de calcetines*

2 CHOOSE A STRATEGY

Would it help us solve the problem if we could keep track of all the sneakers and socks Katie could wear together? *Yes*

The little picture at the top of your paper means that you can make an organized list to help you solve the problem. There is a list started on your paper.

● ¿Les sería de ayuda llevar la cuenta de todos los zapatos y calcetines que Katie se puede poner para poder resolver el problema? *Sí*

El dibujito en la parte de arriba de la página significa que pueden hacer una lista para resolver este problema. Se ha empezado a hacer una lista en sus cuadernos de trabajo.

3 SOLVE IT

sneakers   socks

TEACHING TIP

Provide two pairs of shoes in different colors and two pairs of socks in different colors. Have the children show several different shoe/sock combinations that could be made from the set. Children may note that if the sneakers or socks in each pair don't have to be the same color, the number of combinations will be greater.

1.  and

2.  and

3.  and

4.  and

Look at the list that has been started.

A. **Look at the sneakers in set 1. What color sneakers do you want to show first?** *Red (or yellow)* ● *Rojos (o amarillos)* **What color socks do you want to show first?** *Blue (or green)* ● *Azules (o verdes)* **Color the sneakers and socks in set 1 with those colors. That will be Katie's first set.**

B. **Is there a different color of socks that Katie could wear with the same sneakers?** *Yes* ● *Sí* **Color the socks in set 2 that color. Color the sneakers in set 2 the same color as the sneakers in set 1.**

C. Follow the same procedure for the third and fourth sets.

Solution: *Red sneakers and blue socks*
     red sneakers and green socks
     yellow sneakers and blue socks
     yellow sneakers and green socks
     ● *Zapatos rojos y calcetines azules*
     zapatos rojos y calcetines verdes
     zapatos amarillos y calcetines azules
     zapatos amarillos y calcetines verdes

4 LOOK BACK

Let's look back at the problem to see if your answer fits with what the problem tells you and asks you to find. Listen to the problem again. Read the problem again. **Does your answer fit?**

EXTENSION PROBLEM

How many different sets of sneakers and socks could Katie put on if she had a pair of purple socks, too? *6: red sneakers and blue socks, red sneakers and green socks, red sneakers and purple socks, yellow sneakers and blue socks, yellow sneakers and green socks, yellow sneakers and purple socks*

● **¿Cuántas combinaciones de zapatos y calcetines puede ponerse Katie si también tuviera un par de calcetines morados?** *6: zapatos rojos y calcetines azules; zapatos rojos y calcetines verdes; zapatos rojos y calcetines morados; zapatos amarillos y calcetines azules; zapatos amarillos y calcetines verdes; zapatos amarillos y calcetines morados*

TALK ABOUT IT

Ask questions like, **How can you keep track of which shoes and socks you have used as you make the sets?** ● **¿Cómo pueden llevar la cuenta de los zapatos y medias que ya han usado mientras hacen las combinaciones?**

PRACTICE

Similar Practice Problem: 60

Make an Organized List
Hacer una lista

Content Strands:
Number and Operations, Algebra

Each child needs 2 crayons: red and blue.

5

Tracy's friends are calling to her from outside. They want her to come out and make a snowman. She goes to her closet to get mittens and a cap. She has one pair of striped mittens and one pair of mittens with a diamond pattern. She has one red cap and one blue cap. What are the different sets of snow things that Tracy can wear?

1 FIND OUT

A. **What question do you have to answer to solve the problem?** *What are the different sets of snow things that Tracy can wear?* ● *¿Cuáles son las combinaciones de ropa para la nieve que puede ponerse Tracy?*

B. **How many pairs of mittens does Tracy have in her closet?** *2* **What designs are on them?** *One has stripes and one has diamonds.* ● *Uno es a rayas y el otro un diseño de diamantes.*

C. **How many caps does Tracy have in her closet?** *2* **What color is each?** *One is red and one is blue.* ● *Una es roja y la otra es azul.*

D. **What is a set of snow things?** *One pair of mittens and one cap* ● *Un par de mitones y una gorra* **Which mittens could be in a set?** *Striped or diamond patterned* ● *A rayas y con diseño de diamantes* **Which cap could be in a set?** *Red or blue* ● *Roja o azul*

2 CHOOSE A STRATEGY

Would it help us solve the problem if we could keep track of all the snow things Tracy could wear together? *Yes*

The little picture at the top of your paper means that you can make an organized list to help you solve the problem. We can fill in the list that has been started on your paper.

● **¿Les ayudaría a resolver el problema si pudieran llevar la cuenta de toda la ropa para jugar en la nieve que Tracy se puede poner?** *Sí*

El dibujito en la parte de arriba de la página significa que pueden hacer una lista para resolver este problema. Podemos completar la lista que se ha empezado a hacer en sus cuadernos de trabajo.

③ SOLVE IT

mittens   caps

TEACHING TIP

Have the children practice drawing the mitten designs. Help children understand that you're asking them to sketch these designs quickly to help show which pair of mittens is being worn. Children may simplify the designs to a single diamond and a single stripe.

Look at the list that has been started.

1. and

2. and

3. and

4. and

A. **Look at the pair of mittens in set 1 in the list. Which mittens do you want Tracy to wear first?** *Striped (or diamonds)* ● *A rayas (o con diseño de diamantes)* **Draw that design on the first pair of mittens. Which cap would you like Tracy to wear with those mittens?** *Red (or blue)* ● *Roja (o azul)* **Color the cap with that color. That is her first set.**

B. **Is there a different color cap that Tracy could wear with the same mittens?** *Yes* ● *Sí* **Color the cap in the second set with that color. Then draw the same design on the mittens as you drew in set 1.**

C. **If we just change the color of the hat again, will set 3 be a different set?** *No, it will be the same as set 1.* ● *No, será el mismo que la combinación 1.* **What can we change to make set 3 a different set?** *The design on the mittens* ● *El diseño de los mitones.* For the third and fourth sets, follow the procedure given in steps A and B.

Solution: *Striped mittens and red cap*
      striped mittens and blue cap
      diamond design mittens and red cap
      diamond design mittens and blue cap
● *Mitones a rayas y gorra roja*
      Mitones a rayas y gorra azul
      Mitones con diseño de diamante y gorra rojo
      Mitones con diseño de diamante y gorra azul

④ LOOK BACK

Let's look back at the problem to see if your answer fits with what the problem tells you and asks you to find. Listen to the problem again. Read the problem again. **Does your answer fit?**

EXTENSION PROBLEM

How many different sets of snow things could Tracy wear if she had two pairs of mittens but only one cap? *2 sets*

● **¿Cuántas combinaciones de ropa para jugar en la nieve puede usar Tracy si ella también tuviera dos pares de mitones pero sólo una gorra?** *2 combinaciones*

TALK ABOUT IT

Ask questions like, **Was this second problem easier or more difficult than the first problem? Why?** ● **¿Fue el segundo problema más fácil o más difícil de resolver que el primero?**

PRACTICE

Similar Practice Problem: 60

Make an Organized List
Hacer una lista

6

Yum! Harvey makes very good sandwiches. Harvey has two sandwich spreads in his food box. They are cheese and peanut butter. He has apple bread and onion bread in his food box. When Harvey makes a sandwich, he puts one sandwich spread on one kind of bread. What are the different sandwiches Harvey can make?

❶ FIND OUT

A. **What question do you have to answer to solve the problem?** *What are the different sandwiches Harvey can make?* ● *¿Cuántos sándwiches diferentes puede hacer Harvey?*

B. **How many kinds of bread does Harvey have in his food box?** *2* **What kinds?** *Apple and onion* ● *Manzana y cebolla*

C. **How many kinds of sandwich spreads does Harvey have in his food box?** *2* **What are they?** *Cheese and peanut butter* ● *Queso y mantequilla de maní*

D. **How does Harvey make a sandwich?** *He puts one kind of sandwich spread on one kind of bread.* ● *Harvey le unta un aderezo a una clase de pan.* **Would he make a cheese and peanut butter sandwich?** *No*

E. **What kind of spread can he put on a sandwich?** *Cheese or peanut butter* ● *Queso o mantequilla de maní* **What kind of bread can he use in a sandwich?** *Apple or onion* ● *Manzana o cebolla*

❷ CHOOSE A STRATEGY

Would it help to keep track of all the different sandwiches Harvey can make? *Yes*

What does the little picture at the top of your paper mean? *We can use an organized list to help us solve the problem.*

● **¿Les sería de ayuda llevar la cuenta de los diferentes sándwiches que Harvey puede hacer?** *Sí*

¿Qué significa el dibujito en la parte de arriba de la página? *Que podemos usar una lista para resolver el problema.*

apple   onion

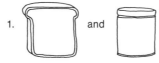

TEACHING TIP

Talk with the children about the word *combinations*. Ask them what the word means and how it relates to this problem.

1. ☐ and ⬭   3. ☐ and ⬭

2. ☐ and ⬭   4. ☐ and ⬭

Look at the list that has been started

A. **Look at the bread for sandwich 1 in the list. What kind of bread do you want to use for the first sandwich?** *Apple (or onion)*
● *Manzana (o cebolla)* **Write the name on the bread. What kind of sandwich spread would you like to put on your first sandwich?** *Cheese (or peanut butter)*
● *Queso (o mantequilla de maní)* **Write the name of the spread on the jar. That is Harvey's first sandwich.**

B. **Is there a different kind of spread that Harvey can put on the same kind of bread?** *Yes* ● *Sí* **Write the name of the different spread on the jar. What name must you write on the bread for sandwich 2?** *The same name as the bread for sandwich 1* ● *El mismo nombre que tiene el pan del sándwich 1*

C. **If you keep using the same kind of bread, can you make the third sandwich different?** *No* **What can you change to make sandwich 3 different?** *The bread*
● *El pan* For sandwiches 3 and 4, follow the procedure given in steps A and B.

Solution: *Apple and peanut butter*
      apple and cheese
      onion and peanut butter
      onion and cheese
   ● *Manzana y mantequilla de maní*
      manzana y queso
      cebolla y mantequilla de maní
      cebolla y queso

4 LOOK BACK

Let's look back at the problem to see if your answer fits with what the problem tells you and asks you to find. Listen to the problem again. Read the problem again. **Does your answer fit?**

EXTENSION PROBLEM

How many different sandwiches could Harvey make if he had three kinds of bread in his food box? *6*
● **¿Cuántos sánwiches diferentes puede hacer Harvey si también tuviera tres clases de pan?** *6*

TALK ABOUT IT

Ask questions like, **How did you keep track of the different combinations of bread and spread as you worked?** ● **¿Qué hicieron para llevar la cuenta de las diferentes combinaciones de pan y aderezo mientras resolvían el problema?**

PRACTICE

Similar Practice Problem: 60

Use or Make a Table
Usar o hacer una tabla

Content Strands:
Number and Operations, Algebra, Data Analysis and Probability

7

Krista is trying to count the goldfish, but they keep hiding under rocks. Lupe gives some clues about how many goldfish there are. Here are Lupe's clues.

- There are more than 5.
- There are fewer than 8.
- There are not 6.

How many goldfish are in the fish bowl?

1 FIND OUT

A. **What question do you have to answer to solve the problem?** *How many goldfish are in the fish bowl?* ● *¿Cuántos peces hay en la pecera?*

B. **What is Krista trying to do?** *Count the goldfish in the bowl.* ● *Trata de contar los peces que hay en la pecera.*

C. **How is Lupe helping Krista find the number of goldfish?** *Lupe is giving Krista some clues.* ● *Lupe le da algunas pistas a Krista.* **What does "clues" mean?** *Hints* ● *Pistas*

D. **What do Lupe's clues tell you about the number of goldfish?** *There are more than 5. There are fewer than 8. There are not 6.* ● *Hay más de 5. Hay menos de 8. No hay 6.*

TEACHING TIP

Review the meaning of phrases like *more than 5* and *fewer than 8*.

---

2 CHOOSE A STRATEGY

Does the problem tell you exactly how many goldfish are in the bowl? *No* Does it give you some clues or hints about how many there are? *Yes*

Would it help us solve the problem if we could see all the numbers that could be the answer? *Yes* The little picture at the top of your paper means that you can use or make a table of numbers to help you solve the problem. The table will help us keep track of numbers as we use the clues.

● ¿Les dice el problema con exactitud cuántos peces hay en la pecera? *No* ¿Les da pistas acerca de cuántos peces hay en la pecera? *Sí*

¿Les ayudaría a resolver el problema si pudieran ver las cantidades de peces que podrían ser la respuesta? *Sí* El dibujito en la parte de arriba de la página significa que pueden usar o hacer una tabla para resolver el problema. La tabla nos ayudará a llevar la cuenta de la cantidad de peces mientras usamos las pistas.

③ SOLVE IT

Look at the table that has been started.

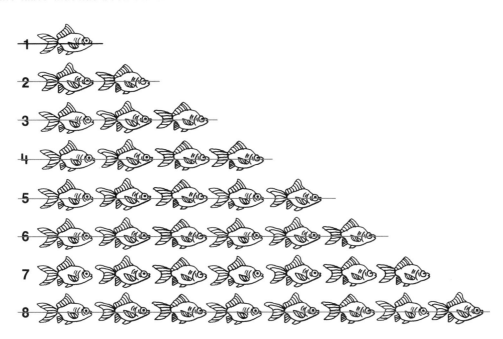

A. **What is the highest number in Lupe's clues?** *8* **That is the highest number in the table.**

B. **Let's start with the first clue: There are more than 5. If there are more than 5 goldfish, could 1 be the number of goldfish in the bowl?** *No* **That is why number 1 is crossed out. Could 2 be the answer?** *No* **Then cross out number 2. Could 3 be the answer?** *No* **Cross it out. 4?** *No* **Cross it out. 5?** *No* **Cross it out. Could 6 be the number of goldfish?** *Yes, it could be.* ● *Sí, puede ser.* **7?** *Yes* ● *Sí* **8?** *Yes* ● *Sí*

C. **Let's use the second clue: There are fewer than 8. Could the number of goldfish be 6?** *Yes* ● *Sí* **Could it be 7?** *Yes* ● *Sí* **Could it be 8?** *No* **Cross it out. Which numbers are left?** *6 and 7* ● *6 y 7*

D. **Here's the third clue: There are not 6. Could there be 6 goldfish in the bowl?** *No* **Which number is left?** *7* **That is the only number that fits all the clues. How many goldfish are in the bowl?**

Solution: *7 goldfish* ● *7 peces*

④ LOOK BACK

Let's look back at the problem to see if your answer fits with what the problem tells you and asks you to find. Listen to the problem again. Make sure that your answer fits with all the clues. Read the problem. **Does your answer fit?**

EXTENSION PROBLEM

What would the answer be if the clues told you there were more than 8 goldfish, fewer than 11, but not 9? *10*

● **¿Qué contestarían si las pistas les dijeran que hay más de 8 peces, menos de 11, pero no hay 9?** *10*

TALK ABOUT IT

Ask questions like, **Which numbers did you include in your table?** ● **¿Qué cantidades anotaron en sus tablas?**

PRACTICE

Similar Practice Problems: 61, 79

8

Aisha's cat had kittens. Tomás wants to count the kittens, but they keep hiding in the barn. Aisha gives Tomás clues about how many kittens there are. Here are Aisha's clues.

• There are fewer than 10.

• There are more than 7.

• There are not 8.

How many kittens did Aisha's cat have?

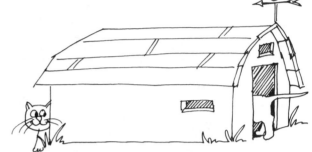

① FIND OUT

A. **What question do you have to answer to solve the problem?** *How many kittens did Aisha's cat have?* ● *¿Cuántos gatitos tuvo la gata de Aisha?*

B. **What is Tomás trying to do?** *Count the kittens of Aisha's cat* ● *Contar los gatitos de la gata de Aisha.* **Why can't Tomas count them?** *They keep hiding in the barn.* ● *Se esconden en el granero.*

C. **How is Aisha helping Tomás?** *She is giving him clues about the number of kittens.* ● *Ella le está dando pistas acerca de cuántos gatitos hay.*

D. **What do Aisha's clues tell you about the number of kittens?** *There are fewer than 10. There are more than 7. There are not 8.* ● *Hay menos de 10. Hay más de 7. No hay 8.*

② CHOOSE A STRATEGY

Does the problem tell you exactly how many kittens Aisha's cat had? *No* **Does it give you some clues or hints about how many there are?** *Yes*

Would it help us solve the problem if we could see all the numbers that could be the answer? *Yes* **The little picture at the top of your paper means that you can make a table of numbers to help you solve the problem. The table will help us keep track of numbers as we use the clues.**

● **¿Les dice el problema con exactitud cuántos gatitos tuvo la gata de Aisha?** *No* **¿Les da pistas acerca de cuántos gatitos hay?** *Sí*

¿Les ayudaría a resolver el problema si pudieran ver las cantidades de gatitos que hay? *Sí* **El dibujito en la parte de arriba de la página significa que pueden usar o hacer una tabla para resolver el problema. La tabla les ayuda a llevar la cuenta de la cantidad de gatitos mientras usamos las pistas.**

Look at the table that has been started.

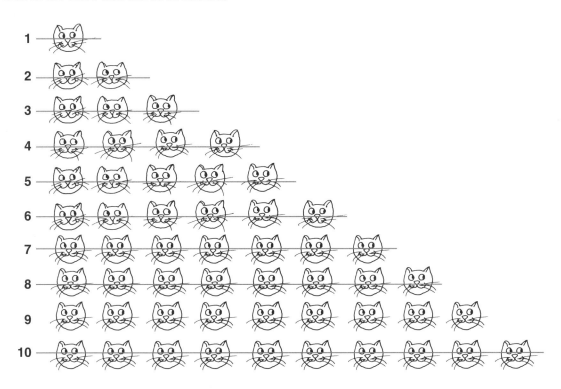

1
2
3
4
5
6
7
8
9
10

A. **What is the highest number in Aisha's clues?** *10* **Is that the highest number in the table?** *Yes* ● *Sí*

B. **Start with the first clue: There are fewer than 10 kittens. If there are fewer than 10 kittens, could 1 be the number of kittens?** *Yes* ● *Sí* **Could 2 be the answer?** *Yes* ● *Sí* **3?** *Yes* ● *Sí* Continue this process through number 9. **Could 10 be the answer?** *No* **Then cross it out.**

C. **Now let's use the second clue: There are more than 7. Is 1 more than 7?** *No* **Then cross out 1. Is 2 more than 7?** *No* **Then cross it out. Is 3 more than 7?** *No* **What other numbers can we cross out?** *4, 5, 6, 7* **What numbers are not crossed out?** *8 and 9* ● *8 y 9*

D. **Here's the third clue: There are not 8. Could the number of kittens be 8?** *No* **Cross it out. What number is left?** *9* **How many kittens did Aisha's cat have?**

Solution: *9 kittens* ● *9 gatitos*

④ **LOOK BACK**

Let's look back at the problem to see if your answer fits with what the problem tells you and asks you to find. Listen to the problem again. Make sure that your answer fits with all the clues. Read the problem. **Does your answer fit?**

EXTENSION PROBLEM

What would the answer be if the clues told you there were fewer than 11 kittens, more than 8, but not 9? *10*

● **¿Qué contestarían si la tercera pista les dijera que hay menos de 11 gatitos, más de 8, pero no hay 9?** *10*

TALK ABOUT IT

Ask questions like, **How did you decide what the highest number would be in your table?** ● **¿Cómo supieron cuál era la cantidad más alta en la tabla?**

PRACTICE

Similar Practice Problems: 61, 79

9

Dusty was giving a treasure hunt for puppies. He hid the bones in funny places. Dusty did not tell the puppies how many bones he hid. He just gave them some clues.

- There are more than 9.
- There are fewer than 12.
- There are not 10.

How many bones did Dusty hide?

❶ FIND OUT

A. **What question do you have to answer to solve the problem?** *How many bones did Dusty hide?* ● *¿Cuántos huesos escondió Dusty?*

B. **What did Dusty do?** *He hid some bones for a treasure hunt.* ● *Él escondió algunos huesos para luego buscarlos como si fueran un tesoro.*

C. **Who will look for the bones in the treasure hunt?** *Puppies* ● *Los cachorritos*

D. **What do Dusty's clues tell you about the number of bones?** *There are more than 9. There are fewer than 12. There are not 10.* ● *Hay más de 9. Hay menos de 12. No hay 10.*

❷ CHOOSE A STRATEGY

Does the problem tell you exactly how many bones Dusty hid? *No* **Does it give you some clues or hints about how many there are?** *Yes*

What does the little picture at the top of your paper mean? *We can use a table of numbers to help us solve the problem.*

● **¿Les dice el problema con exactitud cuántos huesos escondió Dusty?** *No* **¿Les da pistas para saber cuántos huesos hay?** *Sí*

¿Qué significa el dibujito en la parte de arriba de la página? *Que podemos usar una tabla para anotar las cantidades y ayudarnos a resolver el problema.*

TEACHING TIP

Some children may begin to realize that the table doesn't need to begin with 1 if one of the clues states that the answer is greater than a certain number. However, continue working with the numbers shown in the table until all students can come to this realization.

Look at the table that has been started.

A. **Why is 12 the highest number in the table?** *The second clue says the number is less than 12.* ● *La segunda pista dice que hay menos de 12.*

B. **What is the first clue?** *There are more than 9.* ● *Hay más de 9.* **Start with the number 1 in the table. If there are more than 9, could 1 be the number of bones?** *No* **Cross it out. Could 2 be the number?** *No* **3?** *No* **4?** *No* **5?** *No* **6?** *No* **7?** *No* **8?** *No* **Could 9 be the answer?** *No, because there are more than 9.* ● *No, porque hay más de 9.* **Could 10 be the answer?** *Yes* ● *Sí* **11?** *Yes* ● *Sí* **12?** *Yes* ● *Sí*

C. **What is the second clue?** *There are fewer than 12.* ● *Hay menos de 12.* **Could 10 be the answer?** *Yes* ● *Sí* **11?** *Yes* ● *Sí* **12?** *No* **Which numbers are left?** *10 and 11* ● *10 y 11*

D. **What is the third clue?** *There are not 10.* ● *No hay 10.* **Which number can you cross out?** *10* **Cross out 10. Which number is left?** *11* **How many bones did Dusty hide?**

Solution: *11 bones* ● *11 huesos*

Let's look back at the problem to see if your answer fits with what the problem tells you and asks you to find. Listen to the problem again. Make sure that your answer fits with all the clues. Read the problem. **Does your answer fit?**

1 🦴
2 🦴 🦴
3 🦴 🦴 🦴
4 🦴 🦴 🦴 🦴
5 🦴 🦴 🦴 🦴 🦴
6 🦴 🦴 🦴 🦴 🦴 🦴
7 🦴 🦴 🦴 🦴 🦴 🦴 🦴
8 🦴 🦴 🦴 🦴 🦴 🦴 🦴 🦴
9 🦴 🦴 🦴 🦴 🦴 🦴 🦴 🦴 🦴
10 🦴 🦴 🦴 🦴 🦴 🦴 🦴 🦴 🦴 🦴
11 🦴 🦴 🦴 🦴 🦴 🦴 🦴 🦴 🦴 🦴 🦴
12 🦴 🦴 🦴 🦴 🦴 🦴 🦴 🦴 🦴 🦴 🦴 🦴

EXTENSION PROBLEM

What would the answer be if the clues told you there were more than 11, fewer than 14, but not 12? *13*

● **¿Qué contestarían si las pistas les dijeran que hay más de 11, menos de 14, pero no hay 12?** *13*

TALK ABOUT IT

Ask questions like, **Which numbers did you include in your table?** ● **¿Qué cantidades anotaron en sus tablas?**

PRACTICE

Similar Practice Problems: 61, 79

Use Logical Reasoning
Usar la lógica

10

Bob, Peggy, Jeremy, and Doreen are the Hooper children. Each of the children carries things to school in a backpack. Bob's pack is the largest one. Peggy's pack has dots all over it. Doreen's pack does not have a hole in it. Which backpack belongs to each child?

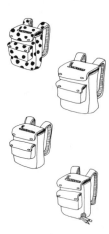

1 FIND OUT

A. **What question do you have to answer to solve the problem?** *Which backpack belongs to each child?* ● *¿Cuál es la mochila de cada niño?*

B. **What are the children's names?** *Bob, Peggy, Jeremy, Doreen* **How many children are in the Hooper family?** *4*

C. **How many backpacks are there in all?** *4*

D. **What do you know about Bob's backpack?** *It's the largest one.* ● *Es la más grande.* **About Peggy's backpack?** *It has dots on it.* ● *Tiene puntos.* **About Doreen's backpack?** *It does not have a hole in it.* ● *No está rota.* **About Jeremy's backpack?** *The problem does not tell about Jeremy's pack.* ● *El problema no da información de la mochila de Jeremy.*

2 CHOOSE A STRATEGY

The little picture at the top of your paper means that you can use a special kind of thinking to solve this problem. It is called logical reasoning.

As we read each clue, we'll look at the pictures. We'll draw a line to the backpack that fits the clue.

● El dibujito en la parte de arriba de la página significa que pueden usar un razonamiento especial para resolver este problema. Ese razonamiento se llama usar la lógica.

Mientras leemos las pistas, observaremos los dibujos. Trazaremos una línea hasta las mochilas que coinciden con las pistas.

Look at the clues and the pictures of the backpacks on your paper.

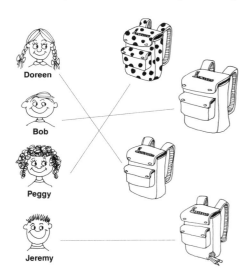

A. **What do you know about Bob's backpack?** *It's the largest one.* ● *Es la más grande.* **Draw a line from Bob to the largest pack.**

B. **What do you know about Peggy's pack?** *It has dots.* ● *Tiene puntos* **Draw a line from Peggy to the pack with dots.**

C. **Which packs must belong to Doreen and Jeremy?** *The two that are left* ● *Las dos que quedan*

D. **What do you know about Doreen's pack?** *It does NOT have a hole in it.* ● *NO está rota.* **If Doreen's pack does not have a hole in it, then which pack must be Doreen's?** *The pack with no hole in it; the second from the bottom* ● *La mochila que no está rota; la segunda desde abajo* **Draw a line from Doreen to the pack without the hole.**

E. **Which of the Hooper children is left?** *Jeremy* **Which pack is left?** *The pack with a hole; the bottom pack* ● *La mochila que está rota, la mochila de abajo* **If Jeremy is the only child left and the pack with the hole is the only pack left, then which pack is Jeremy's?** *The pack with the hole* ● *La mochila que está rota* **Draw a line from Jeremy to the pack with the hole.**

Solution: See above.

④ LOOK BACK

Let's look back at the problem to see if your answer fits with what the problem tells you and asks you to find. Listen to the problem again. Make sure that your answer fits with all the clues. Read the problem. **Does your answer fit?**

EXTENSION PROBLEM

What if the Hoopers traded packs? Jeremy's new pack is the biggest. Bob's new pack has a hole in it. Peggy's new pack does not have dots. Now which pack belongs to each child? *The big pack is Jeremy's, the pack with a hole is Bob's, the dotted pack is Doreen's, and the other pack is Peggy's.*

● **¿Qué pasaría si la familia Hooper intercambiara las mochilas? Si la de Jeremy fuera la más grande, si la de Bob estuviera rota y si la de Peggy no tuviera puntos. ¿Cuál sería la mochila de cada niño?** *La grande es la de Jeremy, la que está rota es la de Bob, la que tiene puntos es la de Doreen y la que queda es la de Peggy.*

TALK ABOUT IT

Ask questions like, **The problem didn't tell you about Doreen's pack. How did you find it?** ● **El problema no les dio información de la mochila de Doreen. ¿Cómo supieron cuál era?**

PRACTICE

Similar Practice Problem: 62

Use Logical Reasoning
Usar la lógica

11

David, James, Maria, and Ruth each have a puppet. David's puppet has the largest ears. Ruth's puppet is wearing a hat. Maria's puppet does not have a long nose. Which puppet belongs to each child?

① FIND OUT

A. **What question do you have to answer to solve the problem?** *Which puppet belongs to each child?* ●*¿Cuál es el títere de cada niño?*

B. **What are the children's names?** *David, James, Maria, Ruth* **How many children are there?** *4*

C. **How many puppets are there in all?** *4* **What do you know about David's puppet?** *It has*

the largest ears. ●*Tiene orejas más grandes.* **About Ruth's puppet?** *It is wearing a hat.* ●*Tiene un sombrero.* **About Maria's puppet?** *It does not have a long nose.* ●*No tiene la nariz larga.* **About James' puppet?** *The problem does not tell about it.* ●*El problema no lo dice.*

② CHOOSE A STRATEGY

The little picture at the top of your paper means that you can use a special kind of thinking to solve this problem. It is called logical reasoning.

As we read each clue, we'll look at the pictures. We'll draw a line to the puppet that fits the clue.

● El dibujito en la parte de arriba de la página significa que pueden usar un razonamiento especial para resolver este problema. Ese razonamiento se llama usar la lógica.

Mientras leemos las pistas, observaremos los dibujos. Trazaremos una línea sobre los títeres que coinciden con las pistas.

3 SOLVE IT

Look at the clues and the pictures of the puppets.

A. **What do you know about David's puppet?** *It has the largest ears.* ● *Tiene las orejas más grandes.* **Draw a line from David to the puppet with the largest ears.**

B. **What do you know about Ruth's puppet?** *It is wearing a hat.* ● *Tiene un sombrero.* **Draw a line from Ruth to the puppet with the hat.**

C. **Which puppets must belong to James and Maria?** *The two that are left; the top and the bottom puppets* ● *Los dos que quedan, los títeres de arriba y de abajo*

D. **What do you know about Maria's puppet?** *It does not have a long nose.* ● *No tiene nariz larga.* **If Maria's puppet does not have a long nose, then which puppet must belong to Maria?** *The top puppet* ● *El títere de arriba* **Draw a line from Maria to the puppet at the top.**

E. **Which child is left?** *James* **Which puppet is left?** *The second puppet; the one with small ears and a long nose* ● *El segundo títere; el que tiene orejas cortas y nariz larga* **If James is the only child left and there is only one puppet left, then which puppet belongs to James?** *The second puppet; the one with small ears and a long nose* ● *El segundo títere, el que tiene orejas cortas y nariz larga* **Draw a line from James to that puppet.**

Solution: See above.

4 LOOK BACK

Let's look back at the problem to see if your answer fits with what the problem tells you and asks you to find. Listen to the problem again. Make sure that your answer fits with all the clues. Read the problem. **Does your answer fit?**

EXTENSION PROBLEM

The children traded puppets. Now the girls have puppets with long noses. Ruth's puppet has big ears. James' puppet wears a hat. Now which puppet belongs to each child?

● **Los niños intercambiaron marionetas. Ahora las niñas tienen títeres con narices largas. El de Ruth tiene orejas grandes, el de James tiene un sombrero. ¿Cuál es el títere de cada uno?**

Solution: From the top, the puppets are David's, Maria's, Ruth's, and James'.

TALK ABOUT IT

Ask questions like, **Did the first clue tell you exactly which puppet belonged to one of the children? How did it help you?** ● **Les dijo la primera pista con exactitud cuál es el títere de cada niño? ¿Les ayudó eso a resolver el problema?**

PRACTICE

Similar Practice Problems: 62

12

Daisy, Bailey, Elton, and Twig have just finished their baths. Now they need to put their collars back on, but they have gotten all mixed up. The tag on Twig's collar is round. The tag on Bailey's collar is square. The tag on Elton's collar is not a hexagon. Which collar belongs to each dog?

① FIND OUT

A. **What question do you have to answer to solve the problem?** *Which collar belongs to each dog?* ● *¿Cuál es el collar de cada perro?*

B. **Which dogs had baths?** *Daisy, Bailey, Elton, Twig* **How many dogs are there?** *4*

C. **How many collars are there in all?** *4* **What do you know about Twig's collar?** *It has*

a round tag. ● *Tiene una medalla redonda.* **About Bailey's collar?** *It has a square tag.* ● *Tiene una medalla cuadrada.* **About Elton's collar?** *Its tag is not a hexagon.* ● *La medalla no es un hexágono.* **About Daisy's collar?** *The problem does not tell about it.* ● *El problema no lo dice.*

② CHOOSE A STRATEGY

The little picture at the top of your paper means that you can use a special kind of thinking to solve this problem. It is called logical reasoning.

As we read each clue, we'll look at the pictures. We'll draw a line to the collar that fits each clue.

● El dibujito en la parte de arriba de la página significa que pueden usar un razonamiento especial para resolver este problema. Ese razonamiento se llama usar la lógica.

Mientras leemos las pistas, observaremos los dibujos. Trazaremos una línea sobre los collares que coinciden con las pistas.

3 SOLVE IT

Look at the clues and the pictures of the dog collars.

A. **What do you know about Twig's collar?** *It has a round tag.* ● *Tiene una medalla redonda.* **Draw a line from Twig to the collar with the circular tag.**

B. **What do you know about Bailey's collar?** *It has a square tag.* ● *Tiene una medalla cuadrada.* **Draw a line from Bailey to the collar with the square tag.**

C. **Which collars must belong to Elton and Daisy?** *The two that are left; the top and bottom collars* ● *Los dos que quedan; los collares de arriba y de abajo*

D. **What do you know about Elton's collar?** *It does NOT have a tag that is a hexagon.* ● *NO tiene una medalla hexagonal.* **If Elton's collar does *not* have a hexagon-shaped tag, then which collar must belong to Elton?** *The one with the heart-shaped tag* ● *El que tiene la medalla en forma de corazón* **Draw a line from Elton to his collar.**

E. **How many dogs are left?** *1* **How many collars are left?** *1* **If only one dog and only one collar are left, then what do you know about that collar?** *It belongs to Daisy, the only dog left.* ● *Es el de Daisy, el único perro que queda.* **Which collar belongs to Daisy?** *The one with the hexagon-shaped tag* ● *El que tiene una medalla en forma de hexágono* **Draw a line from Daisy to her collar.**

Solution: See above.

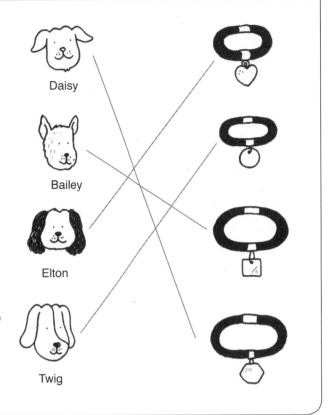

4 LOOK BACK

Let's look back at the problem to see if your answer fits with what the problem tells you and asks you to find. Listen to the problem again. Make sure that your answer fits with all the clues. Read the problem. **Does your answer fit?**

EXTENSION PROBLEM

What if each dog owned a different collar? Daisy's collar does not have a heart-shaped tag. Elton's collar has a square tag. Bailey's collar has a round tag. Which collar belongs to each dog? *Daisy—hexagon, Bailey—circle, Elton—square, Twig—heart*

● **¿Qué pasaría si los perros tuvieran un collar diferente? El collar de Daisy no tiene una medalla en forma de corazón. El de Elton tiene una medalla cuadrada. El de Bailey tiene una medalla redonda. ¿Cuál es el collar de cada perro?** *Daisy—hexágono, Bailey—redonda, Elton—cuadrada, Twig—corazón*

TALK ABOUT IT

Ask questions like, **Does the order of the clues make this problem harder or easier? How?** ● **¿El orden de las pistas hace más difícil o menos difícil resolver el problema? ¿Por qué?**

PRACTICE

Similar Practice Problem: 62

Use or Make a Picture or Diagram
Usar o hacer un dibujo o un diagrama

Content Strands:
Number and Operations,
Algebra, Geometry

13

Susan is going to school. She has to cross 8 bridges on her way. She starts out from her house and crosses 6 bridges. Stop! She dropped her lunch somewhere. Susan turns around and goes back across 2 bridges. She finds her lunch. She turns around again and goes across 4 bridges. Where is Susan now?

1 FIND OUT

A. **What question do you have to answer to solve the problem?** *Where is Susan now?* ● *¿Dónde está Susan ahora?*

B. **Where does Susan start from?** *Her house* ● *Desde su casa* **Where is Susan going?** *To school* ● *A la escuela* **How many bridges does Susan have to cross to get from her house to school?** *8*

C. **How many bridges does Susan cross before she stops?** *6* **What does she do just after she stops?** *Turns around and goes back for her lunch* ● *Ella regresa para buscar su almuerzo* **How many bridges does she cross when she goes back to find her lunch?** *2* **When Susan turns around again, how many bridges does she cross?** *4*

TEACHING TIP

Have students demonstrate the meaning of *turns around and goes back.* Students can act out the problem by stepping over objects you lay on the floor to represent the bridges. To help children keep track of the bridges, reinforce the idea that a bridge is counted only *after* it has been crossed.

2 CHOOSE A STRATEGY

Would it help us to be able to see Susan's house, her school, and the bridges between them? *Yes*

The little picture at the top of your paper means that you can use or make a picture to help you solve the problem. Let's use the picture on your paper so that we can "see" Susan crossing bridges on her way to school.

● **¿Les ayudaría a resolver el problema si pudieran ver la casa de Susan, la escuela y los puentes que hay en el camino a la escuela?** *Sí*

El dibujito en la parte de arriba de la página significa que pueden usar o hacer un dibujo para resolver este problema. Vamos a usar el dibujo que está en los cuadernos de trabajo para poder "ver" a Susan cruzando los puentes en el camino hacia la escuela.

❸ SOLVE IT

Look at the picture that shows Susan's house and the path to school.

Susan's house

Susan's school

A. **Where does Susan start?** *At her house* ●
Desde su casa **Put your finger on Susan's house.**

B. **How many bridges does she cross?** *6* **Move your finger along the path. Go across 6 bridges.**

C. **What does she do when she finds out that she dropped her lunch?** *She stops and turns around.* ● *Ella se detiene y regresa.* **Now is she going toward school or toward her home?** *Toward her home* ● *Va hacia la casa*

D. **How many bridges does she cross now?** *2* **Move your finger across those bridges.**

E. **Susan finds her lunch. Then what does she do?** *She turns around again.* ● *Se da la vuelta y continúa su camino.* **Now is she going toward school or toward her home?** *Toward school* ● *Va hacia la escuela*

F. **How many bridges does she cross?** *4* **Move your finger across those bridges.**

G. **Where is Susan now?** *At school* ● *En la escuela* **How must you show the answer?** *Write an S there.* ● *Escribimos una S ahí.*

Solution: *Susan is at school.* ● *Susan está en la escuela.*

❹ LOOK BACK

Let's look back at the problem to see if your answer fits with what the problem tells you and asks you to find. Listen to the problem again. Make sure that your answer fits with all the clues. Read the problem. **Does your answer fit?**

EXTENSION PROBLEM

The next day, Susan starts out from her house and crosses 6 bridges. Wait! She dropped her notebook somewhere. She turns around and goes back across 5 bridges. She finds her notebook. She turns around again and goes across 4 bridges. Where is Susan now? *Just in front of the sixth bridge from home*

● **Al siguiente día, Susan sale de la casa y cruza 6 puentes. ¡Alto! A ella se le cayó el cuaderno en algún lugar. Ella se regresa y cruza 5 puentes. Susan encuentra el cuaderno. Ella se da la vuelta, continúa su camino y cruza 4 puentes. ¿Dónde está Susan ahora?** *Está frente al sexto puente.*

TALK ABOUT IT

Ask questions like, **Did Susan have a longer walk this time, or in the original problem? Why?**
● **¿Tuvo Susan que caminar más en este problema que en el problema original? ¿Por qué?**

PRACTICE

Similar Practice Problem: 63

14

Barney Bear is going to Bert's birthday party. Barney must pass 8 trees on the way from his home to Bert's home. Barney leaves his home and goes past 6 trees. Oh! Where is his present? Barney dropped it somewhere. He turns around and walks back past 4 trees. There's his present! He takes it and turns around to go toward Bert's home again. He passes 2 trees. Where is Barney now?

1 FIND OUT

A. **What question do you have to answer to solve the problem?** *Where is Barney now?*
● *¿Dónde está Barney Oso ahora?*

B. **Where does Barney start from?** *His home*
● *Desde su casa* **Where is Barney going?** *To Bert's home* ● *A la casa de Bert* **How many trees must Barney pass on the way to Bert's home?** *8*

C. **How many trees does Barney pass before he turns around?** *6* **Why does Barney turn around?** *He sees that he dropped his present somewhere.* ● *Porque se da cuenta que se le cayó el regalo en algún lugar.* **How many trees does Barney pass when he goes back to find his present?** *4* **When Barney turns around after he finds his present, how many trees does he pass?** *2*

2 CHOOSE A STRATEGY

Would it help us to be able to see Barney's home, Bert's home, and the trees between them? *Yes*

The little picture at the top of your paper means that you can use or make a picture to help you solve the problem. Let's use the picture on your paper so that we can "see" Barney passing trees on his way to Bert's party.

● **¿Les ayudaría a resolver el problema si pudieran ver las casas de Barney Oso y de Bert, y los árboles que hay entre sus casas?** *Sí*

El dibujito en la parte de arriba de la página significa que pueden usar o hacer un dibujo para resolver este problema. Vamos a usar el dibujo que está en los cuadernos de trabajo para poder "ver" a Barney pasar por los árboles en su camino hacia la fiesta de Bert.

Look at the picture that shows Barney's home and the path to Bert's home.

A. **Where does Barney start?** *At his home* ● *Desde su casa* **Put your finger on Barney's home.**

B. **How many trees does he pass?** *6* **Move your finger past 6 trees.**

C. **What does he do when he finds out his present is missing?** *He turns around.* ● *Él se regresa.* **Now is he going toward Bert's home or toward his own home?** *Toward his own home* ● *Va hacia su propia casa*

D. **How many trees does he pass as he walks back?** *4* **Move your finger.**

E. **Now what does Barney do?** *He gets the present and turns around again.* ● *Él encuentra el regalo y se da la vuelta para continuar su camino.* **Now is he going toward Bert's home or toward his own home?** *Toward Bert's home* ● *Hacia la casa de Bert*

F. **How many trees does he pass?** *2* **Move your finger.**

G. **Where is Barney now?** *Just past the fourth tree from his home* ● *Justo al pasar el cuarto árbol desde su propia casa* **How must you show the answer?** *Write a B there.* ● *Escribimos una B ahí.*

Solution: *Barney is just past the fourth tree from his home.* ● *Barney justo acaba de pasar por el cuarto árbol desde su propia casa.*

❹ **LOOK BACK**

Let's look back at the problem to see if your answer fits with what the problem tells you and asks you to find. Listen to the problem again. Make sure that your answer fits with all the clues. Read the problem. **Does your answer fit?**

EXTENSION PROBLEM

Where would Barney be now if he had turned around, passed 3 trees to pick up the present, and then stopped to wait for his sister? *Just past the third tree*

● **¿Dónde puede estar Barney ahora si él se hubiera regresado, si hubiera pasado por 3 árboles hasta donde está el regalo y después se hubiera detenido a esperar a su hermana?** *Estaría justo después de haber pasado tres árboles*

TALK ABOUT IT

Ask questions like, **After Barney stopped to wait for his sister, how many bends in the road would he need to go around to reach Bert's home?** ● **Después de que Barney se detiene para esperar a su hermana, por cuántas curvas en el camino tiene que pasar Barney Oso para llegar a la casa de Bert?**

PRACTICE

Similar Practice Problem: 63

Use or Make a Picture or Diagram
Usar o hacer un dibujo o un diagrama

Content Strands:
Number and Operations, Algebra, Geometry

15

Rosa is going to a store to get some balloons. She has to pass 12 light posts on the way from her house to the store. Rosa leaves her house and runs past 10 light posts. Oops! She can't find her money. She turns around and goes back past 8 light posts. She finds her money on the sidewalk. Rosa turns around again and runs past 9 light posts. Where is Rosa now?

1 FIND OUT

A. **What question do you have to answer to solve the problem?** *Where is Rosa now?*
● *¿Dónde está Rosa ahora?*

B. **Where does Rosa start from?** *Her house*
● *Desde su casa* **Where is Rosa going?** *To a store* ● *A la tienda* **How many light posts does Rosa have to pass on her way from home to the store?** *12*

C. **How many light posts does Rosa pass before she turns around?** *10* **Why does Rosa turn around?** *She lost her money.*
● *A ella se le perdió el dinero.* **How many light posts does Rosa pass when she goes back to find her money?** *8* **When Rosa turns around after she finds her money, how many light posts does she pass?** *9*

2 CHOOSE A STRATEGY

What could we use to help us see Rosa's house, the store, and the light posts between them? *The picture on our paper*

What does the little picture at the top of your paper mean? *We can use or make a picture to help solve the problem.*

● **¿Qué podemos usar para ver la casa de Rosa, la tienda y los postes de loz?** *El dibujo que está en los cuadernos de trabajo*

¿Qué significa el dibujito en la parte de arriba de la página? *Que podemos usar o hacer un dibujo para resolver el problema.*

TEACHING TIP

Remind children to use their fingers to trace Rosa's path on the picture and to pass each light post before counting it. You may want to have a student act out the problem before students trace Rosa's path.

Look at the picture of Rosa's house and the path to the store.

A. **Where does Rosa start?** *At her house* ● *Desde su casa* **Put your finger on Rosa's house.**

B. **How many light posts does she run past?** *10*

C. **What does she do when she finds out her money is missing?** *She turns around.* ● *Ella se regresa.* **Now is she going toward the store or toward her home?** *Toward her home* ● *Hacia la casa*

D. **How many light posts does she pass now?** *8*

E. **Then what does Rosa do?** *She finds her money and turns around again.* ● *Ella encuentra el dinero y se da la vuelta para continuar su camino.* **Now is she going toward the store or toward her home?** *Toward the store* ● *Hacia la tienda*

F. **How many light posts does she pass?** *9*

G. **Where is Rosa now?** *Just past the eleventh light post from her house* ● *Justo después del undécimo poste de luz desde su casa* **How must you show the answer?** *Write an R there.* ● *Escribimos una R ahí.*

Solution: *Rosa is just past the eleventh light post from her house.* ● *Rosa justo acaba de pasar el undécimo poste de luz desde su casa.*

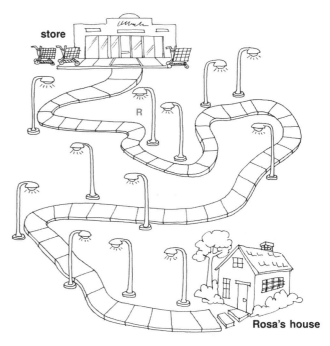

store

R

Rosa's house

Let's look back at the problem to see if your answer fits with what the problem tells you and asks you to find. Listen to the problem again. Make sure that your answer fits with all the clues. Read the problem. **Does your answer fit?**

EXTENSION PROBLEM

Where would Rosa be now if she had passed only 7 light posts on her way back to find her money? *At the store*

● **¿Dónde estaría Rosa ahora si hubiera pasado por 7 postes de luz cuando regresa para buscar el dinero?** *En la tienda*

TALK ABOUT IT

Ask questions like, **Did Rosa go farther all together in this problem, or the original problem?** ● **¿Caminó Rosa más lejos en este problema que en el problema original?**

PRACTICE

Similar Practice Problem: 63

Make an Organized List
Hacer una lista

16

Wally is looking at the yummy food in the lunchroom. He wants to eat 7 pieces of food for lunch today. Wally will take only 2 plates of food. He will eat everything on those plates. What are the 3 different lunches that Wally could buy?

① FIND OUT

A. **What question do you have to answer to solve the problem?** *What are the 3 different lunches that Wally could buy?* ● *¿Cuáles son los 3 diferentes almuerzos que Wally puede comprar?*

B. **What is on each plate that Wally is looking at?** *From left to right: 1 lettuce leaf, 2 beans, 3 tomatoes, 4 celery stalks, 5 radishes, 6 carrots*

● *De izquierda a derecha: 1 lechuga, 2 frijoles, 3 tomates, 4 apios, 5 rábanos, 6 zanahorias*

C. **How many pieces of food does Wally want?** *7* **How many plates will he take?** *2* **If Wally takes the plate of carrots, how many carrots will he eat?** *6* **How do you know?** *He'll eat all the food on the plates he takes.* ● *Él se comerá todo lo que haya en los platos.*

TEACHING TIP

Help students grasp the idea of 2 plates with 7 pieces of food in all by naming pairs of plates and asking whether Wally would buy those plates. Discuss the meaning of *different lunches*.

② CHOOSE A STRATEGY

Would it help us solve the problem if we could keep track of the plates of food that Wally might buy? *Yes*

The little picture at the top of your paper means that you can make an organized list to help you solve the problem. Let's finish the list on your paper.

● **¿Les ayudaría a resolver el problema si pudieran llevar la cuenta de los platos de comida que Wally puede comprar?** *Sí*

● **El dibujito en la parte de arriba de la página significa que pueden hacer una lista para resolver este problema. Vamos a completar la lista que está en los cuadernos de trabajo.**

3 SOLVE IT

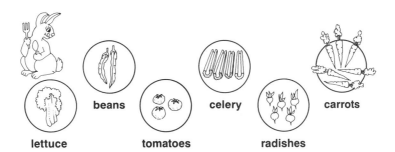

beans   celery   carrots

lettuce   tomatoes   radishes

Look at the list that has been started.

A. **Let's start with the first plate in lunch 1. There is 1 lettuce leaf on it. If Wally wants 7 pieces of food in all, what other plate will he have to get? Count the pieces of food on each plate to find the right plate.** *The plate with 6 carrots* ● *El plato que tiene 6 zanahorias* **Draw 6 carrots on the second plate in lunch 1.**

B. **Would the lunch be the same if you put 6 carrots on the first plate and 1 piece of lettuce on the second plate?** *Yes* ● *Sí* **Can you use either of those plates in a different pair to make 7 pieces of food in all?** *No* **Then cross out those 2 plates in the picture of all the plates. We do not want to show the same lunch again in the list.**

C. **What could you draw on the first plate of lunch 2?** Continue with other combinations of plates until the list is complete.

1. (lettuce) and (   ) = 7 pieces of food

2. (   ) and (   ) = 7 pieces of food

3. (   ) and (   ) = 7 pieces of food

Solution:

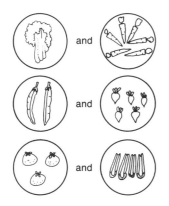

and

and

and

4 LOOK BACK

Let's look back at the problem to see if your answer fits with what the problem tells you and asks you to find. Listen to the problem again. Make sure that your answer fits with all the clues. Read the problem. **Does your answer fit?**

EXTENSION PROBLEM

How many different lunches could Wally have if he can take 2 or 3 plates? 4

● **¿Cuántos almuerzos diferentes puede Wally comprar si tuviera 2 ó 3 platos?** 4

TALK ABOUT IT

Ask questions like, **How many ways are there for Wally to buy three plates of food and get seven pieces of food all together?** ● **¿De cuántas maneras puede Wally comprar tres platos de comida con un total de siete cosas para comer?**

PRACTICE

Similar Practice Problems: 64, 80

Make an Organized List
Hacer una lista

17

Mary is playing a card game with her friends. Mary has cards in her hand. It is her turn to play. She has to lay down 2 cards. The cards must show 9 hearts all together. What 3 different pairs of cards can Mary lay down?

1 FIND OUT

A. **What question do you have to answer to solve the problem?** *What 3 different pairs of cards can Mary lay down?* ● *¿Cuáles son los 3 diferentes pares de naipes que Mary puede poner en la mesa?*

B. **How many hearts are on each of Mary's cards?** *From left to right: 2, 3, 4, 5, 6, 7* ● *De izquierda a derecha: 2, 3, 4, 5, 6, 7*

C. **How many cards must Mary lay down?** *2* **How many hearts must the cards show all together?** *9*

D. **What does "3 different pairs" mean?** *Three sets of 2 cards, with different cards in each set* ● *Tres conjuntos de 2 naipes con diferentes naipes en cada conjunto*

TEACHING TIP

You can review addition facts with sums of 9 by asking the children to tell the number that goes with 3 to make 9, for example.

2 CHOOSE A STRATEGY

Would it help us solve the problem if we could keep track of the cards that Mary could put together to show 9 hearts? *Yes*

The little picture at the top of your paper means that you can make an organized list to help you solve the problem. Let's finish the list started on your paper.

● ¿Les ayudaría a resolver el problema si pudieran llevar la cuenta de los naipes que Mary puede juntar para tener 9 corazones?

El dibujito en la parte de arriba de la página significa que pueden hacer una lista para resolver el problema. Completemos la lista que se ha comenzado a hacer en los cuadernos de trabajo.

3 SOLVE IT

Look at the list that has been started.

A. **Let's start with the first card in pair 1. There are 2 hearts on it. If the pair of cards must show 9 hearts in all, what other card must Mary use with it?** *7* **For pair 1, draw 7 hearts on the second card.**

B. **Would the pair be the same if you put 7 hearts on the first card and 2 hearts on the second card?** *Yes* ● *Sí* **Can you use either of those cards in a different pair to make 9 hearts in all?** *No* **Then cross out the cards with 2 hearts and 7 hearts in the picture of all the cards. We do not want to show the same pair again in the list.**

C. **What could you draw on the first card of pair 2?** Continue with the other pairs of cards until the list is complete.

Solution:

 and

 and

 and

1.   and   [ ]   = 9 hearts

2. [ ]   and   [ ]   = 9 hearts

3. [ ]   and   [ ]   = 9 hearts

4 LOOK BACK

Let's look back at the problem to see if your answer fits with what the problem tells you and asks you to find. Listen to the problem again. Read the problem again. **Does your answer fit?**

EXTENSION PROBLEM

What different pairs of cards could Mary lay down if each pair must show 8 hearts? *2 and 6, 3 and 5*

● **¿Cuántos pares de naipes puede Mary poner en la mesa si cada par debe tener 8 corazones.** *2 y 6, 3 y 5*

TALK ABOUT IT

Ask questions like, **Why couldn't Mary use the 4 to make a pair with 8 hearts?** ● **¿Por qué Mary no puede usar el 4 para hacer un par con 8 corazones?**

PRACTICE

Similar Practice Problems: 64, 80

The Problem Solver   35

Make an Organized List
Hacer una lista

18

Leo and Benji put 6 tin cans on the fence. Each tin can has a number on it. Leo and Benji take turns throwing stones at the cans. Leo and Benji try to knock down 2 cans on each turn. If the numbers on the 2 cans add up to 10, the player gets 10 points. What are the 3 different pairs of cans a player can knock down to get 10 points?

1 FIND OUT

A. **What question do you have to answer to solve the problem?** *What are the 3 different pairs of cans a player can knock down to get 10 points?* ● *¿Cuáles son los 3 diferentes pares de latas que se pueden tumbar para obtener 10 puntos?*

B. **How did Leo and Benji get ready for the game they are playing?** *They put 6 tin cans on the fence.* ● *Ellos ponen 6 latas sobre la cerca.* **What number was on each can?** *From left to right: 8, 4, 7, 2, 3, 6* ● *De izquierda a derecha: 8, 4, 7, 2, 3, 6*

C. **What do the players try to do on each turn?** *Knock down 2 cans* ● *Tumbaron 2 latas* **What happens if the numbers on the cans add up to 10?** *The player gets 10 points.* ● *El jugador obtiene 10 puntos.*

TEACHING TIP
Help students review addition facts with sums of 10.

2 CHOOSE A STRATEGY

What could we use to help us solve the problem? *An organized list*

What does the little picture at the top of your paper mean? *We can make an organized list to help solve the problem.* **Let's finish the list on your paper.**

● **¿Qué podemos usar para resolver el problema?** *Una lista*

¿Qué significa el dibujito en la parte de arriba de la página? *Que podemos hacer una lista para resolver el problema.* **Completemos la lista que está en los cuadernos de trabajo.**

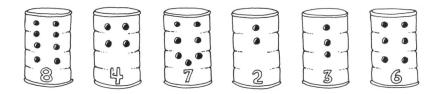

Look at the list that has been started.

A. **Start with the first can in pair 1. It has the number 8 on it. To get a sum of 10, what other can must a player knock down?** *The can marked 2* ● *La lata marcada con el 2* **Write the number 2 on the second can in pair 1.**

1. and = 10 points

B. **Would the pair be the same if a player knocked down the can marked 2 and then the can marked 8?** *Yes* ● *Sí* **Can you use either of those cans in a different pair to make a sum of 10?** *No* **Then cross out the cans marked 2 and 8 in the picture of all the cans. We do not want to show the same pair again in the list.**

2. and = 10 points

C. Continue until the children complete the list.

Solution:

3. and = 10 points

4 **LOOK BACK**

Let's look back at the problem to see if your answer fits with what the problem tells you and asks you to find. Listen to the problem again. Read the problem again. **Does your answer fit?**

EXTENSION PROBLEM

What if the cans showed all the numbers 1 through 9? What other pair could you make to get a sum of 10? *1 and 9*

● **¿Qué pasaría si las latas estuvieran marcadas con los números del 1 al 9? ¿Cuántos otros pares podrían hacer para obtener 10 puntos?** *1 y 9*

TALK ABOUT IT

Ask questions like, **Why couldn't we use a can with five holes in this problem?** ● **¿Por qué no podríamos usar una lata con 5 huecos en este problema?**

PRACTICE

Similar Practice Problems: 64, 80

Guess and Check
Predecir y verificar

19

Juan looked at the toys in Skip's Junk Shop. Skip is selling some little green turtles, rubber birds, squeaky bears, wooden dogs, and fuzzy cats. Juan bought 3 different toys. He paid 12 cents in all. Which 3 toys did Juan buy?

1 FIND OUT

A. **What question do you have to answer to solve the problem?** *Which 3 toys did Juan buy?* ● *¿Cuáles son los 3 juguetes que compró Juan?*

B. **Which toys did Juan look at?** *Turtles, birds, bears, dogs, cats* ● *Tortugas, patitos, ositos, perritos y gatitos*

C. **How many toys did Juan buy?** *3* **Did Juan buy more than one of any kind of toy?** *No, he bought 3 different toys.* ● *No, él compró 3 juguetes diferentes.*

D. **How much does a turtle cost?** *3¢* **How much does a bird cost?** *4¢* **A bear?** *8¢* **A dog?** *9¢* **A cat?** *1¢*

E. **In all, how much did Juan pay for the 3 toys he bought?** *12¢*

2 CHOOSE A STRATEGY

How can we find out which 3 toys cost 12 cents all together? *We can make different groups of 3 toys and add their costs together.*

The little picture at the top of your paper means that you can guess and check to solve this problem. We can make guesses and check to see if our guesses are right. We can start by guessing which 3 toys Juan bought. Then we'll find out if the total cost of that group of toys is 12 cents.

● **¿Cómo podemos saber cuáles son los 3 juguetes que cuestan un total de 12¢?** *Podemos hacer grupos de 3 juguetes diferentes y sumar los precios.*

El dibujito en la parte de arriba de la página significa que pueden predecir y verificar para resolver este problema. Pueden predecir y después verificar para saber si las predicciones anteriores están de acuerdo con las pistas. Podemos empezar por predecir cuáles son los 3 juguetes que compró Juan. Después verificaremos si el total del grupo de juguetes es 12¢.

TEACHING TIP
Let students know that sometimes making, checking, and revising guesses is a time–saving strategy. To show why guessing is appropriate for this problem, you may want to have students start making an organized list of all the possible combinations.

turtle
3 cents

bird
4 cents

bear
8 cents

dog
9 cents

cat
1 cent

A. **Look at the toys in the picture and their costs. Someone make a guess about which 3 toys Juan might have bought.** Have the children write their guesses on their papers. Point out that it helps to keep track of the guesses in a list so that they won't make the same guess a second time.

TEACHING TIP

Ask the children what they should do if their guesses add up to a little more than 12¢. Some children will understand that it is better to change part of a guess in order to get a slightly different total than to start over.

B. The following guesses are only examples. Guess: *Turtle, bird, bear* ● *Tortuga, patito, osito* **How can you check your guess?** *Add the prices of those toys: 3¢ + 4¢ + 8¢ = 15¢.* ● *Sumamos los precios de esos juguetes: 3¢ + 4¢ + 8¢ = 15¢.* **Is the total cost of those toys correct?** *No, it's more than 12¢.* ● *No, el más de 12¢.* **Is the total of your guesses too high or too low?** *Too high* ● *Muy alta* **How can you make your next guess better?** *Change one of the toys to a toy with a lower price.* ● *Cambiamos uno de los jueguetes por otro de precio más bajo.*

C. Guess: *Turtle, bird, cat* ● *Tortuga, patito, gatito* **Check your guess.** *3¢ + 4¢ + 1¢ = 8¢* **Is this the right group of toys?** *No, the total cost is less than 12¢.* ● *No, el total es menos de 12¢.* **How can you make your next guess better?** *Change one of the toys to a toy with a higher price.* ● *Cambiamos uno de los juguetes por otro de precio más alto.*

D. Guess: *Turtle, bear, cat* ● *Tortuga, osito, gatito* **Is this the right group of toys?** *Yes, 3 + 8 + 1 = 12¢, so the total cost is 12¢.* ● *Sí, 3 + 8 + 1 = 12¢, el total es 12¢.*

E. **How must you show the answer?** *Write the names of the toys.* ● *Escribimos los nombres de los juguetes.*

Solution: *Turtle, bear, cat* ● *Tortuga, osito, gatito*

4 **LOOK BACK**

Let's look back at the problem to see if your answer fits with what the problem tells you and asks you to find. Listen to the problem again. Read the problem. **Does your answer fit?**

EXTENSION PROBLEM

What 3 different toys did Juan buy if he paid 14¢ in all? *Dog, bird, cat*

● **¿Cuáles son los 3 diferentes juguetes que compró Juan si pagó un total de 14¢?** *Perrito, patito y gatito*

TALK ABOUT IT

Ask questions like, **Which animal did you guess first to solve this problem? Why?** ● **¿Cuál fue la primera predicción que hicieron para resolver el problema? ¿Por qué?**

PRACTICE

Similar Practice Problems: 65, 81

Guess and Check
Predecir y verificar

20

"Beth, we can only ride for 10 more minutes," said Boris. "Which rides can we take?" Beth looked at the list of rides. She and Boris had tickets for 3 rides. She looked for 3 rides that would take 10 minutes all together. Which 3 different rides can Beth and Boris take?

① FIND OUT

A. **What question do you have to answer to solve the problem?** *Which 3 different rides can Beth and Boris take?* ● *¿A cuáles 3 atracciones pueden Beth y Boris subir?*

B. **How many rides can Beth and Boris take?** *3* **How many minutes could they ride?** *10*

C. **What rides did Beth see on the list?** *Teacup Twist, Ghost Train, Snake, Grasshopper, and Goose Bump* ● *Taza mecedora, Tren*

fantasma, La serpiente, Saltamontes, Piel erizada

D. **How long is a Teacup Twist ride?** *6 minutes* ● *6 minutos* **A Ghost Train ride?** *5 minutes* ● *5 minutos* **A Snake ride?** *4 minutes* ● *4 minutos* **A Grasshopper ride?** *3 minutes* ● *3 minutos* **A Goose Bump ride?** *2 minutes* ● *2 minutos*

② CHOOSE A STRATEGY

How can we find out which 3 rides last 10 minutes all together? *We can make different groups of 3 rides and add the minutes together.*

The little picture at the top of your paper means we can guess and check. Let's start guessing which 3 rides Beth and Boris can take. Then we'll find out if the minutes for those 3 rides add up to 10 minutes.

● **¿Cómo podemos saber cuáles son las 3 atracciones que duran un total de 10 minutos?** *Podemos hacer grupos de 3 atracciones diferentes y sumar el tiempo que dura cada atracción.*

El dibujito en la parte de arriba de la página significa que pueden predecir y verificar para resolver este problema. Vamos a empezar prediciendo a cuáles 3 atracciones Beth y Boris pueden subir. Después hallaremos si los minutos de esas 3 atracciones suman 10 minutos.

TEACUP TWIST	6 minutes
GHOST TRAIN	5 minutes
SNAKE	4 minutes
GRASSHOPPER	3 minutes
GOOSE BUMP	2 minutes

A. **Look at the list of rides and times. Someone make a guess about the 3 rides Beth and Boris might be able to take.** Have the children write the guesses on their papers. Point out that it helps to keep track of the guesses in a list so that they won't make the same guess a second time.

B. The following guess is only an example. Guess: *Teacup Twist, Ghost Train, Snake* ● *Taza mecedora, Tren fantasma, Serpiente* **How will you check your guess?** *Add the minutes for those 3 rides: 6 + 5 + 4 = 15 minutes.* ● *Sumamos los minutos de las 3 atracciones: 6 + 5 + 4 = 15 minutos.* **Is this the right group of rides?** *No, together they'll last longer than 10 minutes.* ● *No, porque duran más de 10 minutos.* **Is the total of your guesses too high or too low?** *Too high* ● *Muy alta* **How can you make your next guess better?** *Change at least one of the rides to a ride that doesn't last as long.* ● *Cambiamos una de las atracciones por otra que no dure mucho tiempo.*

C. Have the children continue to guess until they find the solution.

D. **How must you show the answer?** *Write the names of the rides.* ● *Escribiendo los nombres de las atracciones.*

Solution: *Ghost Train, Grasshopper, Goose Bump*
      ● *Tren fantasma, Saltamontes, Piel erizada*

Let's look back at the problem to see if your answer fits with what the problem tells you and asks you to find. Listen to the problem again. Read the problem. **Does your answer fit?**

EXTENSION PROBLEM

Which 3 different rides could Boris and Beth take if they had 11 minutes left? Two different answers are possible. *Ghost Train, Snake, and Goose Bump or Teacup Twist, Grasshopper, and Goose Bump*

● **¿A cuáles 3 atracciones pueden Boris y Beth subir si les sobran 11 minutos? Dos respuestas son posibles.** *Tren fantasma, Serpiente y Piel erizada o Taza mecedora, Saltamontes y Piel erizada*

TALK ABOUT IT

Ask questions like, **How did you decide which rides to guess first? How did you make your next guess better?** ● **¿Cómo decidieron cuál atracción predecir primero? ¿Qué pueden hacer para que la siguiente predicción sea más acertada?**

PRACTICE

Similar Practice Problems: 65, 81

Guess and Check
Predecir y verificar

21

Patrick wants to make money to buy a special gift for his mom. He needs 8 dollars all together. Patrick's neighbors will pay him to do jobs for them. On Saturday, he did 3 different jobs and earned exactly the right amount! Which 3 jobs did Patrick do?

1 FIND OUT

A. **What question do you have to answer to solve the problem?** *Which 3 jobs did Patrick do?* ● *¿Cuáles son los 3 trabajos que hizo Patrick?*

B. **Look at the pictures of the jobs. Which jobs did Patrick's neighbors have for him to choose from?** *Rake, walk the dog, wash the car, water flowers, put out garbage* ● *Barrer las hojas, sacar al perro, lavar el carro, regar las plantas, sacar la basura*

C. **How many jobs did Patrick do?** *3* **Did Patrick do any job more than once?** *No, he did 3 different jobs.* ● *No, él hizo 3 trabajos diferentes.*

D. **How much could Patrick earn for raking?** *$4* **For walking a dog?** *$2* **For washing a car?** *$5* **For watering flowers?** *$3* **For putting out the garbage?** *$1*

E. **How much did Patrick get for the 3 jobs he did?** *$8*

2 CHOOSE A STRATEGY

What does the little picture at the top of your paper mean? *We can make guesses and check to see if our guesses are right.*

● **¿Qué significa el dibujito en la parte de arriba de la página?** *Que podemos predecir y verificar si nuestra predicción fue correcta.*

3 SOLVE IT

Rake
$4

Walk the dog
$2

Wash the car
$5

Water flowers
$3

Put out garbage
$1

A. **Look at the list of jobs and the amount Patrick can earn for each job. Someone make a guess about the 3 jobs Patrick might have done.** Have the children write the guesses on their papers. Point out that it helps to keep track of the guesses in a list so that they won't make the same guess a second time.

B. The following guess is only an example: *Rake, walk the dog, wash the car* ● *Barrer las hojas, sacar al perro, lavar el carro* **How will you check your guess?** *Add the amounts he can earn for those jobs: $4 + $2 + $5 = $11.* ● *Sumamos las cantidades que él ganó por hacer esos trabajos: $4 + $2 + $5 = $11.* **Is this the right group of jobs?** *No, Patrick would have earned $11 for this group.* ● *No, Patrick hubiera ganado $11 por este grupo.* **Is the total of your guesses too high or too low?** *Too high* ● *Demasiado alta* **How can you make your next guess better?** *Change at least one of the jobs to a job that doesn't pay as much* ● *Cambiamos por lo menos un trabajo por otro que no pague tanto.*

C. Have the children continue to guess until they find the solution.

D. **How must you show the answer?** *Write the names of the jobs.* ● *Escribimos los nombres de los trabajos.*

E. Challenge students to find another solution to the problem.

Solution: *Walk the dog, wash the car, put out garbage; or rake, water flowers, and put out garbage* ● *Sacar al perro, lavar el carro, sacar la basura, o barrer las hojas, regar las plantas sacar la basura*

4 LOOK BACK

Let's look back at the problem to see if your answer fits with what the problem tells you and asks you to find. Listen to the problem again. Read the problem. **Does your answer fit?**

EXTENSION PROBLEM

Which 3 different jobs can Patrick do if he wants to earn 10 dollars? *Rake, wash the car, put out garbage; or walk the dog, wash the car, water flowers*

● **¿Cuáles son los 3 trabajos que Patrick puede hacer si quiere ganar 10 dólares?** *Barrer las hojas, lavar el carro; sacar la basura o sacar al perro, lavar el carro, regar las plantas*

TALK ABOUT IT

Ask questions like, **Can you use your answer to the original problem to help you solve this problem?** ● **¿Les sería de ayuda usar la respuesta del problema original para resolver este problema?**

PRACTICE

Similar Practice Problems: 65, 81

Use or Look for a Pattern
Usar o buscar un patron

22

When Bert blows bubbles, everyone watches. No one else can blow bubbles like he can. Bert blows round bubbles and square bubbles, and he blows them in a pattern! Look at Bert's bubbles and find his pattern. What kind of bubble will Bert blow next?

1 FIND OUT

A. **What question do you have to answer to solve the problem?** *What kind of bubble will Bert blow next?* ● *¿Cuál será figura de la la siguiente burbuja que haga Bert?*

B. **What is special about the way Bert blows bubbles?** *He blows round bubbles and square bubbles, and he blows them in a pattern.* ● *Él hace burbujas redondas y cuadradas, y las hace siguiendo un patrón.* **What is a pattern?** *Something that happens again and again in the same way* ● *Algo que sucede una y otra vez de la misma manera*

C. **Look at the picture on your paper. How many bubbles has Bert blown?** *8* **How many different shapes of bubbles has he blown?** *2* **What kind of bubble did he blow first?** *Square* ● *Cuadrada* **What kind of bubble did he blow next?** *Round* ● *Redonda*

2 CHOOSE A STRATEGY

Would it help us solve the problem if we could figure out what happens again and again when Bert blows bubbles? *Yes*

The little picture at the top of your paper means that looking for a pattern will help you solve the problem.

● **¿Les ayudaría a resolver el problema si pudieran saber qué es lo que sucede una y otra vez cuando Bert hace las burburjas?** *Sí*

El dibujito en la parte de arriba de la página significa que pueden buscar un patrón para resolver el problema.

TEACHING TIP

Ask students to look for examples of patterns around them. Assign a different kind of clap, stomp, snap or tap to each element of the pattern to help the children experience the pattern as they chant it.

③ SOLVE IT

A. **Let's name the shapes of the bubbles, starting with the first bubble.** *Square, round, round, square, round, round, square, round*
   ● *Cuadrada, redonda, redonda, cuadrada, redonda, redonda, cuadrada, redonda*

B. **Can anyone see the pattern in Bert's bubbles?** *First he blows a square bubble, then a round bubble, then another round bubble. Then he starts with a square bubble again.*
   ● *Primero, él hace una burbuja cuadrada, después una redonda, después otra redonda. Él empieza nuevamente con una burbuja cuadrada. You may want to have the children circle each chunk of the pattern they see.*

C. **Did Bert keep blowing bubbles in that pattern?** *Yes* ● *Sí*

D. **What kind of bubble will Bert blow next?** *Round* ● *Redonda*

E. **How must you show the answer?** *Draw the next bubble.* ● *Dibujamos la siguiente burbuja.*

Solution:

④ LOOK BACK

Let's look back at the problem to see if your answer fits with what the problem tells you and asks you to find. Listen to the problem again. Read the problem. **Does your answer fit?**

EXTENSION PROBLEM

What kind of bubble will Bert blow next? *Square*
● **¿Cuál será la figura de la burbuja que hará Bert después?** *Cuadrada*

TALK ABOUT IT

Ask questions like, **What other patterns could Bert make with his square and round bubbles?** ● **¿Qué otro patrón puede hacer Bert con las burbujas cuadradas y redondas?**

PRACTICE

Similar Practice Problem: 66

Use or Look for a Pattern
Usar o buscar un patron

23

Mr. Wing lined up his owls and parrots. They are going to have their picture taken. Mr. Wing used a pattern. Look for his pattern in the line of birds. What will Mr. Wing put in line next, an owl or a parrot?

1 FIND OUT

A. **What question do you have to answer to solve the problem?** *What will Mr. Wing put in line next, an owl or a parrot?* ● *Cuál será la siguiente ave en la fila, ¿el búho o el loro?*

B. **What is Mr. Wing doing?** *Lining up his owls and parrots to have their picture taken* ● *Él está poniendo las aves en fila para tomarles una fotografía.*

C. **What is special about the way Mr. Wing lines up the owls and the parrots?** *He uses a pattern to line them up.* ● *Él usa un patrón para poner a las aves en fila.* **What is a pattern?** *Something that happens again and again in the same way* ● *Es algo que ocurre una y otra vez de la misma manera.*

D. **Look at the picture on your paper. How many birds has Mr. Wing lined up?** 6 **How many different kinds of birds does he have?** 2 **What kind of bird did he put in line first?** *An owl* ● *Un búho*

2 CHOOSE A STRATEGY

Would it help us solve the problem if we could find out what happens again and again in the line of birds? *Yes*

The little picture at the top of your paper means that looking for a pattern will help you solve the problem.

● **¿Les ayudaría a resolver el problema si pudieran saber qué es lo que se repite una y otra vez en la fila de las aves?** *Sí*

El dibujito en la parte de arriba de la página significa que buscar un patrón ayuda a resolver este problema

owl   parrot

A. **Let's name the birds in the line, starting with the first one.** *Owl, owl, parrot, owl, owl, parrot* ● *Búho, búho, loro, búho, búho, loro*

B. **Can anyone see a pattern in Mr. Wing's line?** *He put an owl in line first, then another owl, then a parrot. Then he started with an owl again.* ● *Él primero pone un búho, después pone otro búho y después un loro. Él vuelve a comenzar con un búho.*

C. **Did Mr. Wing keep lining up his students in that pattern?** *Yes* ● *Sí*

D. **What will Mr. Wing put in line next?** *An owl*
   ● *Un búho*

E. **How must you show the answer?** *Write the name of the bird.* ● *Escribimos el nombre de la ave.*

Solution: *Owl* ● *Búho*

4 LOOK BACK

Let's look back at the problem to see if your answer fits with what the problem tells you and asks you to find. Listen to the problem again. Read the problem. **Does your answer fit?**

EXTENSION PROBLEM

What kind of bird will Mr. Wing put in line next?
Another owl

● **¿Cuál ave puso el Sr. Wing después?** *Otro búho*

TALK ABOUT IT

Ask questions like, **How many birds does Mr. Wing line up each time he uses the pattern?** ● **¿Cuántos pájaros pone el Sr. Wing en fila cada vez que él usa el patrón?**

PRACTICE

Similar Practice Problem: 66

Use or Look for a Pattern
Usar o buscar un patron

Content Strands:
Algebra, Geometry

Each child will need 3 crayons: red, green, and blue.

24

Grace Goose is making a string of beads to go around her neck. She is putting beads on the string in a pattern. She is using red beads with circles, green beads with ovals, and blue beads with triangles. Look for Grace's pattern. What kind of bead will Grace put on the string next?

① FIND OUT

A. **What question do you have to answer to solve the problem?** *What kind of bead will Grace put on the string next?* ● *¿Cuál es la siguiente cuenta que Grace pondrá en el hilo?*

B. **What kinds of beads is Grace using?** *Red with circles, green with ovals, and blue with triangles* ● *Rojas con círculos, verdes con óvalos, azules con triángulos*

C. **How many different colors of beads does she have?** *3* **How many different shapes are on the beads?** *3*

D. **What does it mean that Grace is putting the beads on the string in a pattern?** *The order of the beads happens again and again in the same way.* ● *El orden en que las cuentas se ponen una y otra vez de la misma manera.*

E. **Look at the picture on your paper. How many beads has Grace already put on her string?** *10* **What kind of bead did she put on the string first?** *Red with a circle* ● *Roja con un círculo* Read the shapes' and colors' names with students. Have students outline the shape on each bead in the right color.

② CHOOSE A STRATEGY

What does the little picture at the top of your paper mean? *Looking for a pattern will help us solve the problem.*

● **¿Qué significa el dibujito en la parte de arriba de la página?** *Significa que buscar un patrón nos ayuda a resolver este problema.*

48   The Problem Solver

③ SOLVE IT

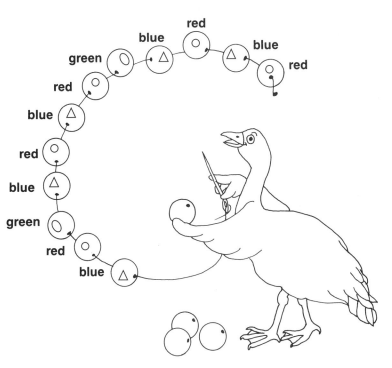

A. **Let's name the colors and shapes on the beads, starting with the first one on the string.** *Red circle, blue triangle, red circle, blue triangle, green oval ...* ●*Roja círculo, azul triángulo, roja círculo, azul triángulo, verde óvalo...*

B. **Can anyone see a pattern in Grace's beads?** *She puts on a red circle bead, a blue triangle bead, a red circle bead, a blue triangle bead, and a green oval bead. Then she starts with a red circle bead again.* ●*Ella pone una cuenta roja círculo, una azul triángulo, una roja círculo, una azul triángulo y una verde óvalo. Después vuelve a comenzar con una cuenta roja círculo.*

C. **Let's check that Grace used that pattern with all the beads.** *Read the beads' colors and shapes again with students.* **Did Grace keep stringing her beads in that pattern?** *Yes* ●*Sí*

D. **What type of bead will Grace put on the string next?** *A red circle bead* ●*Una cuenta roja círculo*

E. **How must you show the answer?** *Draw the bead and color it.* ●*Dibujamos y coloreamos la cuenta.*

Solution:

 red • roja

④ LOOK BACK

Let's look back at the problem to see if your answer fits with what the problem tells you and asks you to find. Listen to the problem again. *Read the problem.* **Does your answer fit?**

EXTENSION PROBLEM

What will the next 3 beads on Grace's string be? *Blue triangle, green oval, red circle*

●**¿Cuáles serán las siguientes 3 cuentas que Grace pondrá en el hilo?** *Azul triángulo, verde óvalo roja círculo*

TALK ABOUT IT

Ask questions like, **How many beads does Grace string each time she uses her pattern?** ●**¿Cuántas cuentas pone Grace cada vez que usa el patrón?**

PRACTICE

Similar Practice Problem: 66

Act Out or Use Objects
Actuarlo o usar objetos

 **Each child needs 4 crayons and four colored counters:
red, yellow, blue, green.**

25

Four fish line up to swim through the castle in their fish tank. The red fish is first in line. The blue fish is in front of the yellow fish. The green fish is in front of the blue fish. What color is the last fish in the line?

1 FIND OUT

A. **What question do you have to answer to solve the problem?** *What color is the last fish in the line?* ● *¿De qué color es el último pez en la fila?*

B. **How many fish are in the line?** *4* **What colors are the fish?** *Red, blue, yellow, green* ● *Rojo, azul, amarillo, verde*

C. **Look at the picture on your paper. Point to the first fish in the line. Now point to the last fish in the line.**

D. **Where is the red fish?** *At the front of the line* ● *El primero en la fila* **Where is the blue fish?** *In front of the yellow fish* ● *Delante del pez amarillo* **Where is the green fish?** *In front of the blue fish* ● *Delante del pez azul* **Do you know where the yellow fish is in the line?** *No, the problem doesn't say.* ● *No, el problema no lo dice.*

2 CHOOSE A STRATEGY

Using objects, or things we can move around, is a good way to solve some problems. The little picture at the top of your paper means that you can use objects or act out the problem to help you solve it.

We can use colored counters or scraps of paper to stand for the fish. What colors should we use? *Red, blue, yellow, and green*

● Usar objetos o cosas que podamos morer de un lado a otro ayuda a resolver algunos problemas. El dibujito en la parte de arriba de la página significa que pueden actuar o usar objetos para resolver este problema.

Puedes usar fichas de colores o pedacitos de papel para representar los peces. ¿Cuáles colores puedes usar? *Rojo, azul, amarillo y verde*

TEACHING TIP
You can relate this problem to students' guess–and–check experiences. After using the definite information the problem gives, students will have to guess the position of the yellow fish. Using objects allows children to make and change guesses easily.

---

③ SOLVE IT

Look at the line of fish on your paper.

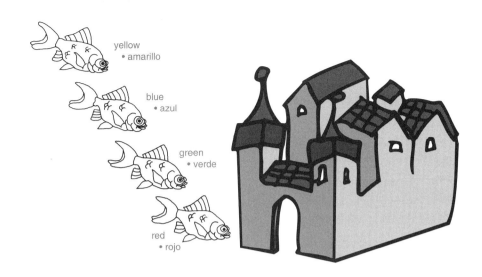

yellow
• amarillo

blue
• azul

green
• verde

red
• rojo

A. **Where shall we put the red counter?** *On the first fish in the line* ● *En el primer pez de la fila*

B. **Where does the problem tell us to put the blue counter?** *In front of the yellow fish* ● *Delante del pez amarillo* **Where is the yellow fish?** *The problem doesn't say.* ● *El problema no lo dice.* **We have to guess where the yellow fish belongs. Let's try the yellow counter on the third fish for now, so there's room for another fish in front of it. Then where does the blue chip go?** *In front of the yellow fish, or on the second fish* ● *Delante del pez amarillo o en el segundo pez*

C. **What does the problem tell us about where to put the green counter?** *It goes in front of the blue fish.* ● *Va delante del pez azul.* **There's no fish there to put it on. Can we move the blue counter so it is behind the yellow counter?** *No, the problem says the blue fish is in front of the yellow fish.* ● *No, el problema dice que el pez azul está delante del pez amarillo.* Encourage students to experiment to find the solution to the next question. **What must we do?** *Move the yellow chip to the fourth fish, move the blue chip to the third fish, and put the green chip on the second fish.* ● *Mover la ficha amarilla al cuarto pez, mover la ficha azul al tercer pez y mover la ficha verde al segundo pez.* **What color is the last fish in line?** *Yellow* ● *Amarillo*

Solution: *Yellow* ● *Amarillo*

④ LOOK BACK

Let's look back at the problem to see if your answer fits with what the problem tells you and asks you to find. Listen to the problem again. Read the problem. After you read each condition, pause and let the students check the position of the colors in their line of fish to be sure the condition is met. **Does your answer fit?**

EXTENSION PROBLEM

What color would the last fish be if the red fish was in front, the green fish was in front of the yellow fish and the yellow fish was in front of the blue fish? *Blue*

● **¿De qué color sería el último pez si el pez rojo fuera el primero en la fila, el pez verde estuviera delante del pez amarillo y el pez amarillo estuviera delante del pez azul?** *Azul*

TALK ABOUT IT

Ask questions like, **How is it helpful to use objects in a problem like this?** ● **¿Cómo ayuda usar objetos para resolver un problema como éste?**

PRACTICE

Similar Practice Problem: 67

Act Out or Use Objects
Actuarlo o usar objetos

 Each child needs 4 scraps of paper.

26

Four boys lined up to go on the Twirl-a-Whirl. Bob was the last one in line. Sam was waiting behind Tom. Pat was behind Sam. Who was first in line?

1 FIND OUT

A. **What question do you have to answer to solve the problem?** *Who was first in line?* ● *¿Quién es el primero en la fila?*

B. **How many boys are in line to go on the Twirl-a-Whirl ride?** *4* **What are their names?** *Bob, Sam, Tom, Pat*

C. **Look at the picture on your paper. Point to the boy who is last in line. Now point to the boy who is first in line.**

D. **Where in the line is Bob?** *At the end* ● *Al final* **Where is Sam?** *Behind Tom* ● *Detrás de Tom* **Where is Pat?** *Behind Sam* ● *Detrás de Sam* **Where is Tom?** *The problem doesn't say.* ● *El problema no lo dice.*

2 CHOOSE A STRATEGY

Would it help us to use things, or objects, to stand for the boys and to be able to move them around? *Yes*

The little picture at the top of the paper means we can act the problem out or use objects to help us solve it. We'll use scraps of paper to stand for the boys. What names shall we write on the scraps of paper? *Bob, Sam, Tom, and Pat*

● **¿Les sería de ayuda usar objetos para representar a los niños y poder moverlos de un lugar a otro?** *Sí*

El dibujito en la parte de arriba de la página significa que pueden actuar o usar objetos para resolver el problema. Usaremos pedacitos de papel para representar a los niños. ¿Cuáles son los nombres que debemos escribir en los pedacitos de papel? *Bob, Sam, Tom, y Pat*

TEACHING TIP

Use some of your students' names in a similar problem, and have the class help those students act out the solution.

Look at the line of boys on your paper.

A. **Where shall we put the name Bob?** *On the last boy in the line* ● *En el último niño en la fila*

B. **Where does the problem tell us to put the name Sam?** *Behind Tom* ● *Detrás de Tom* **Where is Tom?** *The problem doesn't say.* ● *El problema no lo dice.* **We have to guess where Tom belongs. Let's put the name Tom on the second boy in line for now. Then where can we put Sam's name?** *On the third boy* ● *En el tercer niño*

C. **Where does the problem tell us to put the name Pat?** *Behind Sam* ● *Detrás de Sam* **There's no boy to put it on. Can we move Bob?** *No, he must be last in line.* ● *No, tiene que ser el último.* **What must we do?** *Move the name Sam to the second boy in line, move the name Tom to the first boy, and put the name Pat on the third boy.* ● *Mueve el nombre de Sam al segundo niño en fila, mueve el nombe de Tom al primer niño, y el nombre de Pat al tercer niño.* **Who was first in line?** *Tom*

Solution: *Tom*

Let's look back at the problem to see if your answer fits with what the problem tells you and asks you to find. Listen to the problem again. Read the problem. After you read each condition, pause and let the students check the position of the names in the line of boys to be sure the condition is met. **Does your answer fit?**

EXTENSION PROBLEM

Who would be first in line if Tom was behind Pat and Sam was behind Tom, and Bob was still last in line? *Pat*

● **¿Quién sería el primero en la fila si Tom estuviera detrás de Pat, Sam estuviera detrás de Tom y Bob fuera el último en la fila?** *Pat*

TALK ABOUT IT

Ask questions like, **How many different ways did you line up the boys before you found the right answer?** ● **¿De cuántas maneras pusieron en fila a los niños antes hallar la respuesta?**

PRACTICE

Similar Practice Problem: 67

Act Out or Use Objects
Actuarlo o usar objetos

Content Strand:
Algebra, Data Analysis and
Probability

 Each child needs 4 scraps of paper.

27

Four animals live in a tree. The owl lives at the top of the tree. The raccoon lives below the lizard. The lizard lives below the squirrel. Where does each animal live in the tree?

① FIND OUT

A. **What question do you have to answer to solve the problem?** *Where does each animal live in the tree?* ● *¿En qué lugar del árbol vive cada animal?*

B. **How many animals live in the tree?** *4* **Which animals?** *Owl, lizard, squirrel, and raccoon* ● *Búho, lagarto, ardilla y mapache*

C. **Which animal lives at the top of the tree?** *The owl* ● *El búho* **Where does the raccoon live?** *Below the lizard* ● *Debajo del lagarto* **Where does the lizard live?** *Below the squirrel* ● *Debajo de la ardilla* **Do you know where the squirrel lives?** *No, the problem doesn't say.* ● *No, el problema no lo dice.*

TEACHING TIP

Make sure the children understand that if the raccoon is below the lizard, then the lizard is above the raccoon.

---

② CHOOSE A STRATEGY

Would it help us to put the animals' names on objects and move them around on the picture to find out where each animal lives? *Yes*

What does the little picture at the top of your paper mean? *We can use objects or act out the problem to help us solve it.* **What objects can we use?** *Scraps of paper* Have students write the names of the animals on scraps of paper.

● **¿Les sería de ayuda poner los nombres de los animales en objetos y poder moverlos para hallar en qué lugar del árbol viven los animales?** *Sí*

¿Qué significa el dibujito en la parte de arriba de la página? *Que podemos actuar o usar objetos para resolver este problema.* **¿Qué objetos pueden usar?** *Pedacitos de papel.*

3 SOLVE IT

A. **Where shall we put the owl?** *In the space at the top of the tree* ● *En el espacio en la copa del árbol*

B. **Where shall we put the raccoon?** *Below the lizard* ● *Debajo del lagarto* **Do we know yet which space in the tree is the lizard's?** *No* **For now, let's put the lizard off to the side, with the raccoon below it.** Have students place the raccoon below the lizard on their desks beside the paper. **This will help us remember that the raccoon must be below the lizard**.

C. **Where does the squirrel belong?** *Above the lizard* ● *Arriba del lagarto* **Can we put the squirrel on the tree yet, or should we put it on the side with the lizard and the raccoon?** *Since we don't know where the lizard lives, we should put the squirrel on the side, above the lizard.* ● *Como no sabemos en qué lugar del árbol vive el lagarto, podemos poner la ardilla arriba del lagarto.*

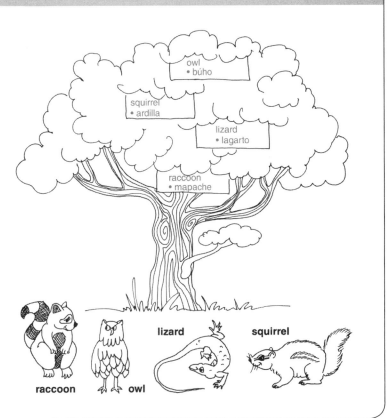

D. **Now you know the order of the squirrel, the lizard, and the raccoon. Do you see three spaces in the tree where those animals can live?** *Yes, the 3 spaces below the owl* ● *Sí, los 3 espacios debajo del búho* **Where shall we put the squirrel?** *Below the owl* ● *Debajo del búho* **Where shall we put the lizard?** *Below the squirrel* ● *Debajo de la ardilla* **Where shall we put the raccoon?** *Below the lizard* ● *Debajo del lagarto* **Where does each animal live in the tree?**

Solution: See the picture.

4 LOOK BACK

Let's look back at the problem to see if your answer fits with what the problem tells you and asks you to find. Listen to the problem again. Read the problem. After you read each condition, pause and let the students check the position of the animals on the tree to be sure the condition is met. **Does your answer fit?**

EXTENSION PROBLEM

In another tree, a raccoon lives above a lizard and below a squirrel, and an owl lives at the top. **Which animal lives at the bottom of the tree?** *Lizard*

● **En otro árbol, un mapache vive arriba del lagarto y debajo de una ardilla, y un búho vive en la copa del árbol. ¿Cuál animal vive en la parte de abajo del árbol?** *Lagarto*

TALK ABOUT IT

Ask questions like, **How did using objects help you solve this problem?** ● **¿Les fue de ayuda usar objetos para resolver el problema?**

PRACTICE

Similar Practice Problem: 67

28

Rose and Rocky Raccoon are going to have a party. They wrote notes to their friends to ask them to come. Rocky wrote faster than Rose did. In the time it took Rose to write 1 note, Rocky wrote 3 notes. Rocky and Rose kept writing in the same way until they finished all the notes. Then Rose put stamps on the 4 notes she wrote. How many notes did Rocky write?

❶ FIND OUT

A. **What question do you have to answer to solve the problem?** *How many notes did Rocky write?* ● *¿Cuántas invitaciones escribió Rocky?*

B. **Who wrote faster, Rose or Rocky?** *Rocky* **How many notes did Rocky write in the time it took Rose to write 1 note?** *3*

C. **How fast did Rocky and Rose keep writing?** *Rocky kept writing 3 notes for every note Rose wrote.* ● *Rocky continuó escibiendo 3 invitaciones por cada invitación que Rose escribía.* **If Rocky wrote 3 notes each time Rose wrote 1 note, how many notes did Rocky write while Rose wrote 2 notes?** *6*

D. **How many notes did Rose write in all?** *4*

❷ CHOOSE A STRATEGY

Would it help us solve the problem if we could keep track of the number of notes each raccoon wrote? *Yes*

The little picture at the top of your paper means that you can make a table of numbers to help you solve the problem.

● **¿Les sería de ayuda llevar la cuenta de la cantidad de invitaciones que escribió cada mapache?** *Sí*

El dibujito en la parte de arriba de la página significa que pueden hacer una tabla para resolver este problema.

3 SOLVE IT

TEACHING TIP
Starting at different numbers, review skip counting by threes.

Look at the table that has been started.

Number of Notes Rose Wrote	1	2	3	4
Number of Notes Rocky Wrote	3	6	9	12

A. **What are we going to keep track of in the top row?** *The number of notes Rose wrote* ● *La cantidad de invitaciones que escribió Rose* **What are we going to keep track of in the bottom row?** *The number of notes Rocky wrote* ● *La cantidad de invitaciones que escribió Rocky*

B. **What number is first in Rose's row?** *1* **What does that mean?** *Rose wrote 1 note.* ● *Rose escribió 1 invitación.* **Look at Rocky's row. How many notes did he write while Rose wrote 1 note?** *3*

C. **What number is next in Rose's row?** *2* **What does that mean?** *Rose finished 2 notes.* ● *Que Rose terminó 2 invitaciones* **Look at Rocky's row. How many notes did he write while Rose wrote 2?** *6*

D. Continue in this way until the children complete the table. Have them record by drawing notes and writing numbers in the table. Then have them write the answer on the line. **Rose wrote 4 notes in all. How many notes did Rocky write?**

Solution: *12 notes* ● *12 invitaciones*

4 LOOK BACK

Let's look back at the problem to see if your answer fits with what the problem tells you and asks you to find. Listen to the problem again. Read the problem. **Look at your table again to see if everything in it is right. Does your answer fit?**

EXTENSION PROBLEM

How many notes would Rocky write if Rose wrote 5 notes? *15*

● ¿Cuántas invitaciones escribe Rocky mientras Rose escribe 5? *15*

TALK ABOUT IT

Ask questions like, **Did you use your table of numbers to help you get started?** ● ¿Usaron la tabla para resolver el problema?

PRACTICE

Similar Practice Problem: 68

Use or Make a Table
Usar o hacer una tabla

Content Strands:
Number and Operations, Algebra

29

Millie and Minnie had a race to see who could get the most crumbs. Millie was much faster than Minnie. In the time it took Minnie to get 1 crumb, Millie picked up 4 crumbs. Millie and Minnie kept picking up crumbs in the same way until they felt footsteps shake the ground. Minnie picked up 4 crumbs in all. How many crumbs did Millie get?

1 FIND OUT

A. **What question do you have to answer to solve the problem?** *How many crumbs did Millie get?* ●*¿Cuántas migajas consiguió Millie?*

B. **Who picked up crumbs faster, Minnie or Millie?** *Millie* **How many crumbs did Millie get each time Minnie got 1?** *4*

C. **How fast did Minnie and Millie keep picking up crumbs?** *Millie kept getting 4 crumbs for every 1 crumb that Minnie got.* ●*Millie continuó consiguiendo 4 migajas por cada 1 migaja que conseguía Minnie.* **If Millie picked up 4 crumbs each time Minnie picked up 1 crumb, how many crumbs did Millie get while Minnie got 2?** *8*

D. **How many crumbs did Minnie pick up in all?** *4*

2 CHOOSE A STRATEGY

Would it help us solve the problem if we could keep track of the number of crumbs each ant picked up? *Yes*

The little picture at the top of your paper means that you can make a table of numbers to help you solve the problem.

● ¿Les ayudaría a resolver el problema si pudieran llevar la cuenta de la cantidad de migajas que cada una consigue? *Sí*

El dibujito en la parte de arriba de la página significa que pueden hacer una tabla para resolver este problema.

TEACHING TIP
Review skip counting by fours.

Look at the table that has been started.

Number of Crumbs Minnie Got	1	2	3	4
Number of Crumbs Millie Got	○○○○	○○○○ ○○○○	○○○○ ○○○○ ○○○○	○○○○ ○○○○ ○○○○ ○○○○
	4	8	12	16

A. **What are we going to keep track of in the top row?** *The number of crumbs Minnie got* ● *La cantidad de migajas que consigue Minnie* **What are we going to keep track of in the bottom row?** *The number of crumbs Millie got* ● *La cantidad de migajas que consigue Millie*

B. **What number is first in Minnie's row?** *1* **What does that mean?** *Minnie picked up 1 crumb.* ● *Minnie recogió 1 migaja.* **Look at Millie's row. How many crumbs did Millie pick up while Minnie picked up 1?** *4*

C. **What number is next in Minnie's row?** *2* **Now look at Millie's row. How many crumbs did Millie pick up while Minnie picked up 2?** *8*

D. Continue until the children complete the table. Then have them record their final answer by writing the number on the line. **Minnie picked up 4 crumbs in all. How many crumbs did Millie get?**

Solution: *16 crumbs* ● *16 migajas*

4 LOOK BACK

Let's look back at the problem to see if your answer fits with what the problem tells you and asks you to find. Listen to the problem again. Read the problem. **Look at your table again to see if everything in it is right. Does your answer fit?**

EXTENSION PROBLEM

How many crumbs would Millie pick up if Minnie picked up 5? *20*

● ¿Cuántas migajas conseguiría Millie si Minnie hubiera conseguido 5? *20*

TALK ABOUT IT

Ask questions like, **How many new columns did you need to add to your table to solve this problem?** ● ¿Cuántas columnas necesitaron añadir a la tabla para resolver el problema?

PRACTICE

Similar Practice Problem: 68

30

Mark and Jon blew up balloons for a party. It took Jon a long time to blow up a balloon. In the time it took Jon to blow up 1 balloon, Mark blew up 2 balloons. The boys kept blowing up balloons in the same way until all the balloons were done. Jon finished 7 balloons. How many balloons did Mark blow up?

① FIND OUT

A. **What question do you have to answer to solve the problem?** *How many balloons did Mark blow up?* ● *¿Cuántos globos infló Mark?*

B. **Who blew up balloons faster, Mark or Jon?** *Mark* **How many balloons did Mark blow up in the time it took Jon to blow up 1 balloon?** *2*

C. **How fast did Mark and Jon keep blowing up balloons?** *Mark kept blowing up 2 balloons for every 1 balloon that Jon did.* ● *Mark continuó inflando 2 globos por cada 1 globo que inflaba Jon.* **If Mark blew up 2 balloons while Jon did 1 balloon, how many balloons did Mark blow up while Jon did 2 balloons?** *4*

D. **How many balloons did Jon blow up in all?** *7*

② CHOOSE A STRATEGY

What could you use to help you keep track of the balloons each boy blew up? *A table of numbers*

What does the little picture at the top of your paper mean? *We can use a table of numbers to help us solve the problem.*

● **¿Qué pueden usar para llevar la cuenta de los globos que infla cada chico?** *Una tabla*

¿Qué significa el dibujito en la parte de arriba de la página? *Significa que podemos hacer una tabla para resolver este problema.*

③ SOLVE IT

TEACHING TIP
You may want to review skip counting by twos.

Look at the table that has been started.

Number of Balloons Jon Blew Up	1	2	3	4	5	6	7
Number of Balloons Mark Blew Up	○○	○○○○	○○○ ○○○	○○○○ ○○○○	○○○○ ○○○○ ○○	○○○○ ○○○○ ○○○○	○○○○ ○○○○ ○○○○ ○○
	2	4	6	8	10	12	14

A. **What are we going to keep track of in the top row?** *The number of balloons Jon did* *Los globos que Jon infló* **In the bottom row?** *The number of balloons Mark did* *Los globos que Mark infló*

B. **What number is in the first box of Jon's row?** *1* **What does that mean?** *Jon blew up 1 balloon.* *Jon infló 1 globo.* **Look at the first box of Mark's row. How many balloons did Mark blow up while Jon did 1?** *2*

C. **What number is in the second box of Jon's row?** *2* **What does that mean?** *Jon blew up 2 balloons.* *Jon infló 2 globos.* **How many balloons did Mark do while Jon did 2?** *4*

D. Continue in this way until the children complete the table. Then have them record their final answer by writing the number on the line. **Jon finished 7 balloons. How many balloons did Mark blow up?**

Solution: *14 balloons* *14 globos*

④ LOOK BACK

Let's look back at the problem to see if your answer fits with what the problem tells you and asks you to find. Listen to the problem again. Read the problem. **Look at your table again to see if everything in it is right. Does your answer fit?**

EXTENSION PROBLEM

How many balloons would Mark blow up if Jon blew up 9 balloons? *18*

 ¿Cuántos globos infla Mark mientras Jon infla 9? *18*

TALK ABOUT IT

Ask questions like, **Did you use the table to solve the problem? Did you find another way to solve it?** **¿Usaron la tabla para resolver el problema? ¿Hallaron otra forma para resolver el problema?**

PRACTICE

Similar Practice Problem: 68

Use or Look for a Pattern
Usar o buscar un patrón

Content Strands:
Number and Operations, Algebra

 Each child will need 16 counters.

31

Lolly likes the capital letter L at the beginning of her name. She likes to make the letter L with blocks. She made her first L with 4 blocks. She added 2 blocks to her first L to make her second L. She added 2 blocks to her second L to make her third L. Lolly keeps using her number pattern. How many blocks will Lolly use to make her fifth L?

1 FIND OUT

A. **What question do you have to answer to solve the problem?** *How many blocks will Lolly use to make her fifth L?* ● *¿Cuántos bloques necesita Lolly para hacer su quinta letra L?*

B. **What is Lolly making?** *Capital L's* ● *La L mayúscula* **What is she using to make them?** *Blocks* ● *Bloques*

C. **How many blocks did Lolly use to make her first L?** *4* **How many blocks did she add to her first L to make her second L?** *2* **How many blocks did she add to her second L to make her third L?** *2* **Was Lolly making her L's larger or smaller?** *Larger* ● *Más grande* **How much larger did she make the L each time?** *2 blocks larger than the L before* ● *2 bloques más grande que la L anterior*

D. **How is Lolly using a number pattern to make the L's larger?** *She is adding the same number of blocks, 2, again and again.* ● *Ella añade la misma cantidad de bloques, 2, una y otra vez.*

2 CHOOSE A STRATEGY

Did Lolly add the same number of blocks each time she made another L? *Yes*

The little picture at the top of your paper means that using a pattern will help you solve the problem. You can also use the pictures, the table on your paper, and some blocks.

● **¿Añadió Lolly la misma cantidad de bloques cada vez que hizo otra L?** *Sí*

El dibujito en la parte de arriba de la página significa que pueden usar un patrón para resolver este problema. También pueden usar los dibujos, la tabla que está en los cuadernos de trabajo y algunos bloques.

Number of Lolly's L	Number of Blocks in L
1st	4
2nd	6
3rd	8
4th	10
5th	12

1st

2nd

3rd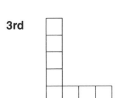

A. **The table will help you keep track of how many blocks are in each L.** Help the children examine the table. **How many blocks did Lolly use to make her first L?** *4* **Look at the picture of her first L. Now use your blocks to make Lolly's first L.**

B. **How many blocks did Lolly add to make her second L?** *2* **Add 1 block on each end of Lolly's first L. How many blocks are in Lolly's second L?** *6*

C. **How many blocks did Lolly add to make her third L?** *2* **Add 1 block on each end of Lolly's second L. How many blocks are in Lolly's third L?** *8*

D. **How many blocks will Lolly add to make her fourth L?** *2* **Add those blocks. How many blocks will be in Lolly's fourth L?** *10* **Record that in the table.**

E. The children can make the fifth L or use the pattern in the table to complete the table. **How many blocks will Lolly use to make her fifth L?**

Solution: *12 blocks* ● *12 bloques*

Let's look back at the problem to see if your answer fits with what the problem tells you and asks you to find. Listen to the problem again. Read the problem. **Does your answer fit?**

EXTENSION PROBLEM

How many blocks will Lolly use to make her sixth L? *14*

●**¿Cuántos bloques necesita Lolly para hacer su sexta L?** *14*

TALK ABOUT IT

Ask questions like, **Did you use the blocks or the table to solve the problem? Did you find a different way to solve it?** ● **¿Usaron los bloques o la tabla para resolver el problema? ¿Hallaron otra forma para resolver el problema?**

PRACTICE

Similar Practice Problem: 69

Use or Look for a Pattern
Usar o buscar un patrón

32

Beth is counting the fruit on the plum tree in her back yard. The first day, Beth counted 5 plums. The next day, there were 3 new plums. Each day, there were 3 new plums. How many plums in all were on the plum tree on the sixth day?

1 FIND OUT

A. **What question do you have to answer to solve the problem?** *How many plums in all were on the plum tree on the sixth day?* ● *¿Cuántas ciruelas en total hay en el árbol el sexto día?*

B. **What is Beth counting?** *Plums* ● *Ciruelas* **Where are the plums?** *On her plum tree* ● *En el árbol*

C. **How many plums did Beth count on the first day?** *5*

D. **How many new plums were there on the second day?** *3* **Then how many plums were there in all on the second day?** *8* **How many new plums were there the next day?** *3 more* ● *3 más*

2 CHOOSE A STRATEGY

Does something keep happening again and again in the same way in this problem? *Yes* **What number pattern did Beth notice?** *There were always 3 new plums added each day.*

The little picture at the top of your paper means that you can use a pattern to help you solve the problem. You can also use the table of numbers on your paper. You may draw the plums if that will help you answer the question.

● **¿Hay algo que se repite una y otra vez de la misma manera en este problema?** *Sí* **¿Cuál patrón numérico notó Beth?** *Siempre había 3 nuevas ciruelas cada día.*

El dibujito en la parte de arriba de la página significa que pueden usar un patrón para resolver este problema. También pueden usar la tabla en sus cuadernos de trabajo. Pueden dibujar las ciruelas si eso les ayuda a contestar la pregunta.

1st 🫐 🫐 🫐 🫐 🫐

2nd 🫐 🫐 🫐 🫐 🫐 🫐 🫐 🫐

3rd 🫐 🫐 🫐 🫐 🫐 🫐 🫐 🫐 🫐 🫐 🫐

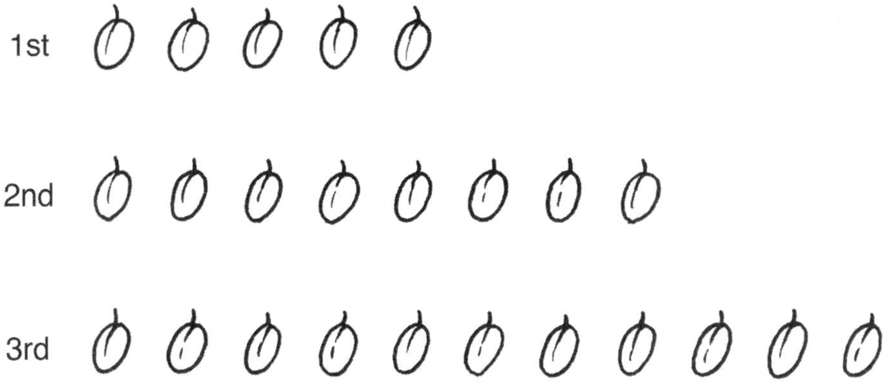

Day	Number of Plums
1st	5
2nd	8
3rd	11
4th	14
5th	17
6th	20

Look at the pictures of the plums on your paper.

A. **How many plums were on the tree the first day?** 5 **Look at the picture of the plums for the second day. How many new plums did Beth see on the second day?** 3 **How many plums were there all together on the second day?** 8

B. **How many new plums did Beth see on the third day?** 3 **How many plums were there all together on the third day?** 11 Have students record 11 and all subsequent numbers of plums in the table.

C. **How many new plums did Beth see on the fourth day?** 3 **How many plums were there all together on the fourth day?** 14 Have the children complete the table. **How many plums in all were on the plum tree on the sixth day?**

Solution: *20 plums* ● *20 ciruelas*

4 LOOK BACK

Let's look back at the problem to see if your answer fits with what the problem tells you and asks you to find. Listen to the problem again. Read the problem. **Does your answer fit?**

EXTENSION PROBLEM

How many plums would there be on the seventh day? 23

● **¿Cuántas ciruelas tendrá el árbol el séptimo día?** 23

TALK ABOUT IT

Ask questions like, **How did you use the pattern to solve this problem?** ● **¿Les fue de ayuda usar un patrón para resolver este problema?**

PRACTICE

Similar Practice Problem: 69

Use or Look for a Pattern
Usar o buscar un patrón

Content Strands:
Number and Operations, Algebra

33

The frogs had a jumping contest. They jumped over a row of stones. They put 3 stones in the row for game 1. They added 3 more stones to the row for game 2. They added 3 more stones to the row for game 3. The frogs kept using the same number pattern to add stones to the row. How many stones were in the row for game 6?

❶ FIND OUT

A. **What question do you have to answer to solve the problem?** *How many stones were in the row for game 6?* ● *¿Cuántas rocas tiene la fila del el salto 6?*

B. **What were the frogs doing?** *Having a jumping contest* ● *Tienen una comptencia de salto.* **What were they jumping over?** *A row of stones* ● *Una fila de rocas*

C. **How many stones were in the row they jumped over in game 1?** *3* **How many stones did they add to the row for game 2?** *3* **How many did they add for game 3?** *3* **Were the frogs making the row longer or shorter each time?** *Longer* ● *Más larga*

❷ CHOOSE A STRATEGY

What does the little picture at the top of your paper mean? *We can use a pattern to solve this problem.*

What number pattern did the frogs use to make the row longer for each game? *They always added 3 stones to the row to make the row for the next game.* **Use that pattern and the number table on your paper. You may also draw the stones if that will help you answer the question.**

● **¿Qué significa el dibujito en la parte de arriba de la página?** *Significa que podemos usar un patrón para resolver este problema.*

¿Cuál es el patrón numérico que usaron los sapitos para hacer que las filas fueran más largas para cada salto? *Añadieron 3 rocas a la fila del siguiente salto.* **Usen el patrón y la tabla en los cuadernos de trabajo. También pueden dibujar las rocas si eso les ayuda a responder la pregunta.**

3 SOLVE IT

Look at the pictures of the stones on your paper.

Game	Number of Stones in the Row
1st	3
2nd	6
3rd	9
4th	12
5th	15
6th	18

Game 1 ○ ○ ○

Game 2 ○ ○ ○ ○ ○ ○

Game 3 ○ ○ ○ ○ ○ ○ ○ ○ ○

A. **How many stones did the frogs use in the row for game 1?** *3* **Look at the pictures of the row for game 1 and the row for game 2. How many stones did the frogs add to make the row for game 2?** *3* **How many stones were in the row for game 2?** *6*

B. **How many stones did they add to make the row for game 3?** *3* **How many stones were in the row for game 3?** *9* Have students record 9 and all subsequent numbers of stones in the table.

C. **How many stones did they add to the row for game 4?** *3* **How many stones were in the row for game 4?** *12*

D. **Now add the stones to the row for game 5.** Have the children complete the table. **How many stones were in the row for game 6?**

Solution: *18 stones* ● *18 rocas*

4 LOOK BACK

Let's look back at the problem to see if your answer fits with what the problem tells you and asks you to find. Listen to the problem again. Read the problem. **Does your answer fit?**

EXTENSION PROBLEM

How many stones will the frogs use in game 8? *24*
● **¿Cuántas rocas usarán los sapitos para el salto 8?** *24*

TALK ABOUT IT

Ask questions like, **How many stones will the frogs use in game 7?** ● **¿Cuántas rocas usarán los sapitos para el salto 7?**

PRACTICE

Similar Practice Problem: 69

Act Out or Use Objects
Actuarlo o usar objetos

 Each child will need 8 counters.

34

The Pet Café is just for pets. They come from all over the neighborhood to enjoy special treats. Today there are 8 pets at the café. They are sitting at 3 tables. There are 5 pets in all at table A and table B. There are 7 pets in all at table B and table C. How many pets are at each table?

1 FIND OUT

A. **What question do you have to answer to solve the problem?** *How many pets are at each table?* ● *¿Cuántas mascotas hay en cada mesa?*

B. **How many pets are at the café today?** *8* **How many tables are the pets using?** *3*

C. **How many pets in all are sitting at table A and table B?** *5*

D. **How many pets in all are sitting at table B and table C?** *7*

TEACHING TIP
Have the class find several different ways to separate 8 volunteers into 3 groups.

---

2 CHOOSE A STRATEGY

Would it help us solve the problem if we could use objects to stand for the pets, and then move the objects from table to table and count them? *Yes*

The little picture at the top of your paper means that you can use objects or act out the problem to help you solve it. Let's use counters to stand for pets. How many will we need? *8*

● **¿Les sería de ayuda para resolver el problema si pudieran usar objetos para representar a las mascotas y moverlas de mesa en mesa y poder contarlas?** *Sí*

El dibujito en la parte de arriba de la página significa que pueden actuar o usar objetos para resolver este problema. Usaremos fichas para representar las mascotas. ¿Cuántas fichas necesitarán? *8*

③ SOLVE IT

Look at the drawing of the three tables.

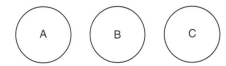

A. **Put some counters on each table to show how many pets you think are at that table.** The following answers are based on a guess of 3 counters at table A, 2 at table B, and 3 at table C. **How many counters did you put at table A?** *3* **Table B?** *2* **Table C?** *3*

B. **The first clue says there are 5 pets in all sitting at table A and table B. Count the counters on your first two tables. Are there 5 in all?** *Yes* ● *Sí* If students' guesses don't satisfy the first clue, have them rearrange their counters now.

C. **Listen to the clue about table B and table C: there are 7 pets in all at table B and table C. How many pets should be sitting at those two tables in all?** *7* **Look at your counters. Do the counters at table B and table C add up to 7?** *No, only 5* ● *No, sólo 5*

D. **If your answers are not right, change the number of counters at each table. Keep trying different ways until your solution fits the clues. Remember to use the clues in the problem as you work.** The children may use logic to adjust their guess as in the following example, or they may experiment with the counters until they find the right answer. **Do we need more pets or fewer pets at tables B and C?** *2 more* ● *2 más* **Where can we get more pets?** *From table A* ● *De la mesa A* **Let's take 2 from table A.** Guide the children to understand that the 2 counters must go on table B to satisfy the first clue.

E. **How many pets are at each table?**

Solution: *Table A—1 pet, Table B—4 pets, Table C—3 pets* ● *Mesa A—1 mascota, Mesa B—4 mascotas, Mesa C—3 mascotas*

④ LOOK BACK

Let's look back at the problem to see if your answer fits with what the problem tells you and asks you to find. Listen to the problem again. Read the problem. **Does your answer fit?**

EXTENSION PROBLEM

What if there were 6 pets in all at Tables A and B, and 4 pets in all at Tables B and C? How many pets would be at each table? *A—4, B—2, C—2*

● *¿Qué pasaría si hubiera un total de 6 mascotas en las mesas A y B y un total de 4 mascotas en las mesas B y C? ¿Cuántas mascotas habría en cada mesa?* *A—4, B—2, C—2*

TALK ABOUT IT

Ask questions like, **How does moving objects around help you solve the problem?** ● *¿Les fue de ayuda usar los objetos para resolver el problema?*

PRACTICE

Similar Practice Problems: 70, 82

Act Out or Use Objects
Actuarlo o usar objetos

Each child needs 12 counters.

35

Skyler is making a dozen mud pies. They are oh, so ooey gooey! Skyler puts the mud pies on 3 plates to bake in the sun. There are 6 mud pies in all on plate A and plate B. There are 8 pies in all on plate B and plate C. How many mud pies are on each plate?

1 FIND OUT

A. **What question do you have to answer to solve the problem?** *How many mud pies are on each plate?* ● *¿Cuántos pasteles de barro hay que cada plato?*

B. **How many mud pies is Skyler making?** *A dozen* ● *Una docena* **How many is a dozen?** *12*

C. **How many plates are there?** *3*

D. **How many mud pies in all are on plate A and plate B?** *6*

E. **How many mud pies in all are on plate B and plate C?** *8*

2 CHOOSE A STRATEGY

Would it help us solve the problem if we could use objects to stand for the mud pies, and then move the objects from plate to plate and count them? *Yes*

The little picture at the top of your paper means that you can use objects or act out the problem to help you solve it. Let's use counters to stand for mud pies. How many will we need? *12*

● **¿Les ayudaría a resolver el problema si pudieran usar objetos para representar los pasteles de barro y moverlos de plato en plato y poder contarlos?** *Sí*

El dibujito en la parte de arriba de la página significa que pueden actuar o usar objetos para resolver este problema. Usaremos fichas para representar los pasteles de barro. ¿Cuántas fichas necesitarán? *12*

TEACHING TIP

Have the class find different ways to separate 12 items into 3 groups.

Look at the picture of the three plates.

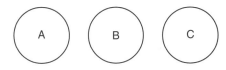

A. **Put some counters on each plate to show how many mud pies you think are on that plate.** The following answers are based on a guess of 6 counters on plate A, 4 on plate B, and 2 on plate C. **How many counters did you put at plate A?** *6* **Plate B?** *4* **Plate C?** *2*

B. **The first clue says there are 6 mud pies in all on plate A and plate B. Count the pies on your first two plates. Are there 6 in all?** *No, there are too many.* ● *No, son muchos.*

C. **If your answers are not right, change the number of counters on each plate. Keep trying different ways until your solution fits the clues. Remember to use the clues in the problem as you work.** The children may use logic to adjust their guesses as in the following example, or they may experiment with the counters until they find the right answer. **Do we need more pies or fewer pies on plates A and B?** *4 fewer* ● *4 menos* **Let's take 4 from plate A. Where can we put them?** *On plate C* ● *En el plato C* **The second clue says there should be 8 pies on plates B and C. Do we have 8 pies on those plates?** *No, we have 10, which is 2 too many.* ● *No, tenemos 10 y eso es 2 de más.* **If we take some of the pies we added to plate C away, could we put them on plate A or B?** *No, we can't add any more to plate A or B.* ● *No, no podemos añadir más al plato A o B.* **Where can we take the 2 pies from?** *Plate B* ● *El plato B* **Where can we put them?** *Plate A* ● *El plato A*

D. **How many mud pies are on each plate?**

Solution: *Plate A—4, plate B—2, plate C—6*
　　　　　 ● *Plato A—4, plato B—2, plato C—6*

Let's look back at the problem to see if your answer fits with what the problem tells you and asks you to find. Listen to the problem again. Read the problem. **Does your answer fit?**

EXTENSION PROBLEM

What if there were 10 mud pies in all on plates A and B, and 9 mud pies in all on plates B and C? How many mud pies would be on each plate? Remember that there are 12 pies in all. *A—3, B—7, C—2*

● **¿Qué sucedería si hubieran 10 pasteles de barro en total en los platos A y B y 9 en los platos B y C? ¿Cuántos pasteles de barro habría en cada plato? Recuerden que sólo hay 12 pasteles.** *A—3, B—7, C—2*

TALK ABOUT IT

Ask questions like, **How does moving objects around help you?** ● **¿Les fue de ayuda mover los objetos?**

PRACTICE

Similar Practice Problems: 70, 82

Act Out or Use Objects
Actuarlo o usar objetos

 Each child needs 11 counters.

36

Steamy Swamp is the perfect place for frogs. There are frogs on logs all over the swamp! There are 11 frogs sunning on 3 logs. There are 9 frogs in all on log A and log B. There are 6 frogs in all on log B and log C. How many frogs are on each log?

1 FIND OUT

A. **What question do you have to answer to solve the problem?** *How many frogs are on each log?* ● *¿Cuántos sapitos hay en cada tronco?*

B. **How many frogs are sunning on logs?** *11*

C. **How many logs are there?** *3*

D. **How many frogs in all are on log A and log B?** *9*

E. **How many frogs in all are on log B and log C?** *6*

2 CHOOSE A STRATEGY

What does the little picture at the top of your paper mean? *We can use objects or act out the problem.*

We'll move counters around on the picture of the three logs. What will each counter stand for? *A frog* **How many will we need?** *11*

● **¿Qué significa el dibujito en la parte de arriba de la página?** *Significa que podemos actuar o usar objetos para resolver este problema.*

Movamos las fichas por el dibujo de los 3 troncos. ¿Qué representará cada ficha? *Un sapito* **¿Cuántas fichas se necesitarán?** *11*

TEACHING TIP
Remind the children that this type of problem involves guessing and checking. If children are reluctant to guess, explain that guesses are just starting points, and they are not meant to be perfect right away.

---

③ SOLVE IT

Look at the picture of the three logs.

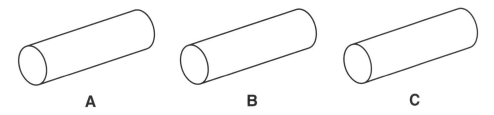

A   **B**   **C**

A. **Put some counters on each log to show how many frogs you think are on that log.** The following answers are based on a guess of 4 counters on log A, 4 on log B, and 3 on log C. **How many counters did you put at log A?** *4* **Log B?** *4* **Log C?** *3*

B. **The first clue says there are 9 frogs in all on log A and log B. Count the frogs on your first two logs. Are there 9 in all?** *No, only 8* ● *No, sólo 8*

C. **If your answers are not right, change the number of counters on each log. Keep trying different ways until your solution fits the clues. Remember to use the clues in the problem as you work.** The children may use logic to adjust their guesses as in the following example, or they may experiment with the counters until they find the right answer. **Do we need more frogs or fewer frogs on logs A and B?** *1 more* ● *1 más* **Where can we get 1 more frog?** *From log C* ● *Del tronco C* **Let's take 1 from log C.** Guide the children to understand that the counter must go on log A to satisfy the second clue.

D. **How many frogs are on each log?**

Solution: *Log A—5 frogs, log B—4 frogs, log C—2 frogs* ● *Tronco A—5 sapitos, tronco B—4 sapitos, tronco C—2 sapitos*

④ LOOK BACK

Let's look back at the problem to see if your answer fits with what the problem tells you and asks you to find. Listen to the problem again. Read the problem. **Does your answer fit?**

EXTENSION PROBLEM

What if there were 10 frogs in all on logs A and B, and 2 frogs in all on logs B and C? How many frogs would be on each log? *A—9, B—1, C—1*

● ¿Y si hay 10 sapitos en los troncos A y B, y 2 sapitos en los troncos B y C? ¿Cuántos sapitos hay entonces en cada tronco? *A—9, B—1, C—1*

TALK ABOUT IT

Ask questions like, **Was this problem harder or easier than the original problem? Why?** ● ¿Fue este problema más difícil o más fácil de resolver que el problema original?

PRACTICE

Similar Practice Problems: 70, 82

Use or Make a Table
Usar o hacer una tabla

Content Strands:
Number and Operations, Algebra

37

Chuck and Dino rode in a bike parade. Chuck led the parade on his 2-wheel bike. Dino rode on his 3-wheel bike behind Chuck's bike. The rest of the monkeys rode 3-wheel bikes behind Dino's bike. There were 5 bikes all together in the parade. Chuck and Dino put streamers on every wheel in the parade. How many wheels were in the parade?

1 FIND OUT

A. **What question do you have to answer to solve the problem?** *How many wheels were in the parade?* ● *¿Cuántas ruedas en total hay en el desfile?*

B. **Who led the bike parade?** *Chuck* **What was he riding?** *His 2-wheel bike* ● *Su bicicleta de 2 ruedas* **Who came next in the parade?** *Dino* **What was he riding?** *His 3-wheel bike* ● *Su bicicleta de 3 ruedas* **Were any other**

monkeys in the parade? *Yes* ● *Sí* **What were they riding?** *3-wheel bikes* ● *Bicicletas de 3 ruedas*

C. **How many bikes were in the parade all together?** *5* **Were Chuck's bike and Dino's bike part of those 5?** *Yes* ● *Sí*

D. **What did Chuck and Dino put on the wheels of the bikes?** *Streamers* ● *Banderines*

TEACHING TIP
Make sure the children see that every bike after Chuck's has 3 wheels. Then help the children prepare to solve this problem by counting on by threes from different numbers.

---

2 CHOOSE A STRATEGY

Would it help us to be able to keep track of the wheels as more bikes are added behind Chuck's bike? *Yes*

The little picture at the top of your paper means that you can use a table of numbers to help you solve the problem. Let's use the table on your paper.

● **¿Sería de ayuda llevar la cuenta de las ruedas a medida que las bicicletas detrás de la bicicleta de Chuck aumentan?** *Sí*

El dibujito en la parte de arriba de la página significa que pueden usar una tabla para resolver este problema. Usaremos la tabla que está en los cuadernos de trabajo.

Look at the table that has been started.

Number of Bikes in the Parade	1	2	3	4	5
Number of Wheels in the Parade	2	5	8	11	14

A. **What are we going to keep track of in the top row?** *The number of bikes in the parade* ● *La cantidad de bicicletas que participan en el desfile* **What are we going to keep track of in the bottom row?** *The total number of wheels on the bikes in the parade* ● *El total de la cantidad de ruedas de las bicicletas que participan en el desfile*

B. **What number is in the first box of the Bikes row?** *1* **What does that mean?** *1 bike, Chuck's bike* ● *1 bicicleta, la de Chuck* **How many wheels were on Chuck's bike?** *2* **Look at the number in the Wheels row. How many wheels are in the parade so far?** *2*

C. **With 1 bike behind Chuck's bike, how many bikes are there in all?** *2* **How many wheels are on the second bike, Dino's bike?** *3* **With 2 bikes in the parade, how many wheels are there in all?** *5*

D. **How many wheels were on every bike after Chuck's?** *3* **How many more wheels are there in the parade each time you add a bike?** *3*

E. **With 3 bikes in the parade, how many wheels are there in all?** *8*

F. Continue in this way until the children complete the table. Then have them record their answer by writing the number on the line.

Solution: *14 wheels* ● *14 ruedas*

Let's look back at the problem to see if your answer fits with what the problem tells you and asks you to find. Listen to the problem again. Read the problem. **Look at your table again to see if everything in it is right. Does your answer fit?**

EXTENSION PROBLEM

How many wheels would be in the parade if there were five 3-wheel bikes behind Chuck's bike? *17*

● **¿Cuántas ruedas habrían en el desfile si hubieran cinco bicicletas de 3 ruedas detrás de la bicicleta de Chuck?** *17*

TALK ABOUT IT

Ask questions like, **How could counting by threes help you solve the problem?** ● **¿Por qué contar de tres en tres les puede ayudar a resolver el problema?**

PRACTICE

Similar Practice Problem: 71

Use or Make a Table
Usar o hacer una tabla

38

It was summertime and the sun was hot. Dawn opened a lemonade stand. She sold lemonade with ice in it. Her friend Carl came to buy some lemonade. Carl paid 4 cents for his first glass of lemonade and 2 cents for each glass of lemonade after that. Carl kept drinking lemonade. At two o'clock, Carl drank his fifth glass of lemonade. How much money did Carl pay Dawn for all the lemonade he drank?

1 FIND OUT

A. **What question do you have to answer to solve the problem?** *How much money did Carl pay Dawn for all the lemonade he drank?* ● *¿Cuánto dinero le pagó Carl a Dawn por todas las limonadas que él se bebió?*

B. **What is Dawn doing?** *Selling lemonade* ● *Vendiendo limonada* **What is Carl doing?** *Buying lemonade* ● *Comprando limonada*

C. **How many glasses of lemonade did Carl buy from Dawn?** *5*

D. **How much money did Carl pay for each glass of lemonade?** *4¢ for his first glass and 2¢ for each other glass* ● *4¢ por el primer vaso y 2¢ por eada siguiente vaso*

2 CHOOSE A STRATEGY

Would it help us to be able to keep track of the money Carl paid as he drank each glass? *Yes*

The little picture at the top of your paper means that you can use a table of numbers to help you solve the problem. Let's use the table on your paper.

● **¿Les sería de ayuda poder llevar la cuenta del dinero que Carl paga por cada vaso de limonada?** *Sí*

El dibujito en la parte de arriba de la página significa que pueden usar una tabla para resolver este problema. Usaremos la tabla que está en los cuadernos de trabajo.

TEACHING TIP
Ask students to find and describe the pattern in this problem.

Look at the table that has been started.

Number of Glasses of Lemonade	1	2	3	4	5
How Much Money Carl Paid in All	4¢	6¢	8¢	10¢	12¢

A. **What are we going to keep track of in the top row?** *The number of glasses of lemonade Carl drank* ● *La cantidad de vasos de limonada que bebió Carl* **What are we going to keep track of in the bottom row?** *How much money Carl paid in all* ● *Cuanto pagó Carl en total*

B. **What number is in the first box of the Glasses row?** *1* **What does that mean?** *1 glass of lemonade* ● *1 vaso de limonada* **Look at the number in the Money row. How much money did Carl pay so far?** *4¢*

C. **How much money did Carl have to pay for each glass after the first one?** *2¢*

D. **What number is in the second box of the Glasses row?** *2* **What does that mean?** *2 glasses of lemonade* ● *2 vasos de limonada* **Look at the number in the Money row. How much money did Carl pay in all for 2 glasses?** *6¢*

E. Continue in this way until the children complete the table. Then have them record the final answer by writing the number on the line.

Solution: *12¢*

 LOOK BACK

Let's look back at the problem to see if your answer fits with what the problem tells you and asks you to find. Listen to the problem again. Read the problem. **Look at your table again to see if everything in it is right. Does your answer fit?**

EXTENSION PROBLEM

How much money would Carl have to pay if he drank 8 glasses of lemonade? *18¢*

● **¿Cuánto tendría que pagar Carl si se hubiera bebido 8 vasos de limonada?** *18¢*

TALK ABOUT IT

Ask questions like, **How much money would Carl pay for the sixth glass?** ● **¿Cuánto dineron pagaría Carl por el sexto vaso de limonada?**

PRACTICE

Similar Practice Problem: 71

Use or Make a Table
Usar o hacer una tabla

Content Strands:
Number and Operations, Algebra

39

"It's time for the Pig Picnic!" called out the 4 pigs in the Oink family. Other pig families hurried over to join in the fun. The Curly family came first. Then the Snuffle family, the Snort family, and the Snout family came to the Pig Picnic. There were 3 pigs in each of those families. There were 5 pig families in all at the picnic. They ate lots of corn! How many pigs were there in all at the picnic?

1 FIND OUT

A. **What question do you have to answer to solve the problem?** *How many pigs were there in all at the picnic?* ● *¿Cuántos cerditos en total fueron al picnic?*

B. **What did the Oink family do?** *Invited other pigs to their picnic* ● *Invitaron a otros cerditos a su picnic.* **What other pig families came to the Pig Picnic?** *The Curly family, the Snuffle family, the Snort family, and the Snout family* ● *Las familias Curly, Snuffle, Snort y Snout* **How many pig families were there in all at the picnic?** *5*

C. **How many pigs were in the Oink family?** *4* **How many pigs were there in each of the families that joined the Oinks for the picnic?** *3*

2 CHOOSE A STRATEGY

What does the little picture at the top of your paper mean? *We can make a table of numbers to help solve the problem.*

You can use the table of numbers on your paper to keep track of the number of pigs as more families joined the picnic.

● **¿Qué significa el dibujito en la parte de arriba de la página?** *Significa que puedemos tabla para resolver este problema.*

Pueden usar la tabla de los cuadernos de trabajo para llevar la cuenta de la cantidad de cerditos que van al picnic a medida que las familias van llegando.

③ SOLVE IT

Look at the table that has been started.

Number of Families	1	2	3	4	5
Number of Pigs in All	4	7	10	13	16

A. **What are we going to keep track of in the first row?** *The number of families at the picnic* ● *El total de las familias en el picnic* **What are we going to keep track of in the second row?** *The number of pigs at the picnic* ● *El total de cerditos en el picnic*

B. **What number is in the first box of the Families row?** *1* **What does that mean?** *1 family, the Oink family* ● *1 familia, la familia Oink* **With 1 family, how many pigs are at the picnic?** *4*

C. **How many pigs are in each family that joins the Oinks?** *3* **With 2 families, how many pigs are there at the picnic?** *7*

D. **With 3 families, how many pigs are there at the picnic?** *10* **How many more pigs are there at the picnic each time you add one more family?** *3*

E. Continue in this way until the children complete the table and find the answer. Then have them write the number on the line.

Solution: *16 pigs* ● *16 cerditos*

④ LOOK BACK

Let's look back at the problem to see if your answer fits with what the problem tells you and asks you to find. Listen to the problem again. Read the problem. **Look at your table again to see if everything in it is right. Does your answer fit?**

EXTENSION PROBLEM

How many pigs would be at the picnic if 5 families joined the Oinks? *19*

● **¿Cuántos cerditos estarían en el picnic si hubieran tenido 5 familias?** *19*

TALK ABOUT IT

Ask questions like, **How many families were at the picnic in all? Can you use your table to find the answer? Can you use any other strategy to find the answer?** ● **¿Cuántas familias hay en total en el picnic? Pueden usar sus tablas para hallar la respuesta? ¿Pueden usar otra estrategia para hallar la respuesta?**

PRACTICE

Similar Practice Problem: 71

Each child will need 25 counters.

40

Simon Squirrel's cousins are coming to visit him next week. He has been getting food ready for their visit. On Monday he cracked 1 nut. On Tuesday he cracked 3 nuts. On Wednesday he cracked 5 nuts, and on Thursday he cracked 7 nuts. Simon is following a number pattern, so he knows how many nuts he will crack on Friday. How many nuts will he crack on Friday?

1 FIND OUT

A. **What question do you have to answer?**
How many nuts will Simon crack on Friday?
●*¿Cuántas nueces cascará Simón el viernes?*

B. **Why has Simon been cracking nuts?** *He is getting food ready for his cousins' visit next week.* ●*Él está preparando la comida para la visita de sus primos en la próxima semana.*

C. **How many nuts did Simon crack on Monday?** *1* **On Tuesday?** *3* **On Wednesday?** *5* **On Thursday?** *7*

D. **How can Simon know how many nuts he will crack on Friday?** *Because he is following a number pattern.* ●*Porque él está siguiendo un patrón numérico.*

2 CHOOSE A STRATEGY

Would it help us solve the problem if we knew Simon's number pattern? *Yes*

The little picture at the top of your paper means that looking for a pattern will help us solve the problem. Let's use some counters to help us "see" the nuts that Simon cracked each day. You can put the counters under the names of the days in the table on your paper.

● **¿Les sería de ayuda saber cuál es el patrón que usa Simón para resolver el problema?** *Sí*

El dibujito en la parte de arriba de la página significa que pueden buscar un patrón para resolver este problema. Usaremos fichas para "ver" las nueces que Simón casca diariamente. Pueden poner las fichas debajo de los días de la semana en la tabla de los cuadernos de trabajo.

③ SOLVE IT

Look at the table on your paper.

Monday	Tuesday	Wednesday	Thursday	Friday
1	3	5	7	9

A. **How many nuts did Simon crack on Monday?** *1* **Put 1 counter under Monday. How many nuts did Simon crack on Tuesday?** *3* **Put 3 counters under Tuesday. How many nuts did Simon crack on Wednesday?** *5* **Put 5 counters under Wednesday. How many on Thursday?** *7* **Put 7 counters under Thursday.**

B. **Now look at the groups of counters. What do you notice?** *Simon cracked 2 more nuts on Tuesday than on Monday, 2 more nuts on Wednesday than on Tuesday, and 2 more nuts on Thursday than on Wednesday.* ● *Simón cascó 2 nueces más el martes que el lunes, 2 más el miércoles que el martes y 2 más el jueves que el miércoles.*

C. **What is the number pattern that Simon is following?** *Each day he cracks 2 more nuts than on the day before.* ● *Cada día, él casca 2 nueces más que el día anterior.*

D. **How many nuts will Simon crack on Friday?** *9*

Solution: *9 nuts* ● *9 nueces*

TEACHING TIP

Talk about naming number patterns in order to talk about them more easily. Simon's pattern could be called a "plus two" pattern. Practice naming a few other patterns, such as 10, 8, 6, 4 ... (a "minus two" pattern).

④ LOOK BACK

Let's look back at the problem to see if your answer fits with what the problem tells you and asks you to find. Listen to the problem again. Read the problem. **Does your answer fit?**

EXTENSION PROBLEM

If Simon keeps following his number pattern, how many nuts will he crack on Saturday? *11*

● **Si Simón sigue este patrón, ¿cuántas nueces cascará el sábado?** *11*

TALK ABOUT IT

Ask questions like, **How did using the table and the number pattern help you solve this problem?** ● **¿Les fue de ayuda usar la tabla y el patrón numérico para resolver este problema?**

PRACTICE

Similar Practice Problem: 72

Use or Look for a Pattern
Usar o buscar un patrón

Content Strands:
Number and Operations, Algebra

41

There are lots of tadpoles in the small pond behind Trudy's house. Trudy put her net into the pond, and 3 tadpoles swam into it. She put her net in again, and 6 tadpoles swam into it. She put her net in again, and 9 tadpoles swam into it. Trudy could see that the tadpoles were following a number pattern. She put her net in again. How many tadpoles swam into Trudy's net the fourth time she put it into the pond?

1 FIND OUT

A. **What question do you have to answer to solve the problem?** *How many tadpoles swam into Trudy's net the fourth time she put it into the pond?* ● *¿Cuántos renacuajos cayeron en la red la cuarta vez que Trudy puso la red en el estanque?*

B. **What did Trudy do?** *She put her net into the pond behind her house.* ● *Ella puso la red en el estanque que está detrás de su casa.*

C. **How many tadpoles swam into Trudy's net the first time she dipped it into the pond?** *3* **The second time?** *6* **The third time?** *9*

D. **What is special about the way the tadpoles swam into the net each time Trudy put it in the pond?** *They followed a number pattern.* ● *Ellos siguen un patrón numérico.*

2 CHOOSE A STRATEGY

Would it help us to know the number pattern the tadpoles followed? *Yes* **The little picture at the top of your paper means that looking for a pattern will help us solve this problem.**

Would it help us to be able to keep track of the tadpoles that swam into the net each time? *Yes* **You can make marks or draw tadpoles in the table on your paper.**

● ¿Sería de ayuda saber cuál es el patrón que siguen los renacuajos? *Sí* **El dibujito en la parte de arriba de la página significa que pueden buscar un patrón para resolver este problema.**

¿Sería de ayuda llevar la cuenta de los renacuajos que cada vez caen en la red? *Sí* **Pueden poner marcas o dibujar los renacuajos en la tabla o en el cuaderno de trabajo.**

Look at the table on your paper.

1st Time	2nd Time	3rd Time	4th Time
√ √ √ 3	√ √ √ √ √ √ 6	√ √ √ √ √ √ √ √ √ 9	√ √ √ √ √ √ √ √ √ √ √ √ 12

A. **How many tadpoles swam into Trudy's net the first time she put it into the pond?** *3* **Make 3 marks under "1st Time." How many tadpoles swam into the net the second time?** *6* **Make 6 marks under "2nd Time." The third time?** *9*

B. **Now look at the groups of marks. What do you notice?** *The number of tadpoles goes up by 3 each time.* ● *La cantidad de renacuajos aumenta 3 cada vez.*

C. **What is the number pattern that the tadpoles followed?**
3 more tadpoles swam into the net each time than the time before. ● *3 renacuajos cayeron en la red más que la vez anterior.*

D. **How many tadpoles swam into Trudy's net the fourth time she put it into the pond?** *12*

Solution: *12 tadpoles* ● *12 renacuajos*

 LOOK BACK

Let's look back at the problem to see if your answer fits with what the problem tells you and asks you to find. Listen to the problem again. Read the problem. **Does your answer fit?**

EXTENSION PROBLEM

If the tadpoles keep following this number pattern, how many of them will swim into Trudy's net the eighth time she puts it into the pond? *24*

● *Si los renacuajos continúan cayendo en la red siguiendo este patrón, ¿cuántos renacuajos caerían en la red de Trudy la octava vez que ella pone la red en el estanque?* *24*

TALK ABOUT IT

Ask questions like, **How many will swim into the net the 6th time? The 7th?** ● *¿Cuántos renacuajos caerían en la red la sexta vez? ¿Cuántos caerían la séptima vez?*

PRACTICE

Similar Practice Problem: 72

Use or Look for a Pattern
Usar o buscar un patrón

Content Strands:
Number and Operations, Algebra

42

There are 12 people standing in line for the swan boat ride. The first boat comes by, and some people get on. Now there are 10 people in line. After the second boat comes by, there are 8 people left in line. The third boat comes by. Now there are 6 people left in line. The number of people in line keeps changing in the same way. How many people are left in line after the fourth boat comes by?

1 FIND OUT

A. **What question do you have to answer to solve the problem?** *How many people are left in line after the fourth boat comes by?* ● *¿Cuántas personas quedan en la fila cuando el cuarto barco sale?*

B. **What are the people waiting for?** *A swan boat ride* ● *Dar un paseo en el barco cisne*

C. **How many people are waiting in line at first?** *12* **After the first boat comes by to pick up passengers, how many people** are left in line? *10* **How many people are left after the second boat picks up its passengers?** *8* **After the third boat?** *6*

D. **What is special about the way the line keeps changing?** *The number of people keeps changing in the same way.* ● *La cantidad de personas continúan cambiando de la misma manera.*

2 CHOOSE A STRATEGY

What do we call something that happens again and again in the same way? *A pattern* **Would it help us to know the number pattern that was happening in the line of people?** *Yes* **The little picture at the top of your paper means that looking for a pattern will help you solve this problem.**

Would it help us to be able to keep track of the number of people in line? *Yes* **You can make marks or draw stick people in the table on your paper.**

● **¿Qué se dice cuando algo se repite una y otra vez de la misma manera?** *Se dice que hay un patrón.* **¿Les ayudaría a resolver el problema si supieran cuál es el patrón numérico de lo que sucede con las personas que están esperando en fila?** *Sí* **El dibujito en la parte de arriba de la página significa que pueden buscar un patrón para resolver este problema.**

¿Sería de ayuda llevar la cuenta de las personas que esperan en fila? *Sí* **Pueden poner marcas o dibujar figuras de personas o palitos en la tabla o en el cuaderno de trabajo.**

Look at the table on your paper.

At First	After 1st Boat	After 2nd Boat	After 3rd Boat	After 4th Boat
√ √ √ √ √ √ √ √ √ √ √ √ 12	√ √ √ √ √ √ √ √ √ √ 10	√ √ √ √ √ √ √ √ 8	√ √ √ √ √ √ 6	√ √ √ √ 4

A. **How many people were waiting in line at first?** *12* **Make 12 marks under "At First." How many people were left in line after the first swan boat picked up its passengers?** *10* **After the second boat?** *8* **After the third boat?** *6*

B. **Now look at the groups of marks. What do you notice?** *The line goes down by 2 people each time.* ● *La fila tiene 2 personas menos cada vez.*

C. **What is the number pattern that is happening in the line?** *2 people get on the boat each time, so the number of people goes down by 2.* ● *Cada vez, 2 personas se van en el barco, por eso la fila tiene 2 personas menos.*

D. **How many people are left in line after the fourth boat comes by?** *4*

Solution: *4 people* ● *4 personas*

TEACHING TIP
Ask the children how the pattern in this problem is different from the patterns in Problems 40 and 41.

---

4 LOOK BACK

Let's look back at the problem to see if your answer fits with what the problem tells you and asks you to find. Listen to the problem again. Read the problem. **Does your answer fit?**

EXTENSION PROBLEM

How many more boats could come by before nobody would be left in line? *2*

● **¿Cuántos barcos más tendrán que salir para que no queden personas esperando en fila?** *2*

TALK ABOUT IT

Ask questions like, **How did your table help you solve this problem?** ● **¿Les fue de ayuda usar la tabla para resolver este problema?**

PRACTICE

Similar Practice Problem: 72

Work Backwards
Trabajar hacia atrás

Each child will need 20 counters.

43

Herman and Polly say Frank catches the most fish because he has the best worms. Maybe they are right. Frank Fox does catch fish! Today he caught 5 more fish than Polly caught. Polly Pig pulled up 4 more fish than Herman did. Herman Rabbit caught only 2 fish. How many fish did Frank catch?

❶ FIND OUT

A. **What question do you have to answer to solve the problem?** *How many fish did Frank catch?* ● *¿Cuántos pescados pescó Frank?*

B. **Who catches the most fish?** *Frank* **What do you know about how many fish Frank caught today?** *He caught 5 more than Polly caught.* ● *Él pescó 5 más de los que pescó Polly.* **Then what do you have to know before you can find out how many fish Frank caught?** *How many fish Polly caught* ● *La cantidad que pescó Polly*

C. **What do you know about how many fish Polly caught today?** *She caught 4 more fish than Herman did.* ● *Ella pescó 4 pescados más que los que pescó Herman.* **Then what do you have to know before you can find out how many fish Polly caught?** *How many fish Herman caught* ● *Cuántos pescados pescó Herman*

D. **How many fish did Herman catch today?** *2*

❷ CHOOSE A STRATEGY

Does the problem tell us the number of fish Frank caught? *No* Polly? *No* Herman? *Yes* Herman's number came at the end of the problem. It looks like we'll have to work backwards from the end of the problem to the beginning.

The little picture at the top of your paper means that working backwards will help us solve this problem. We will use things that we can move around, too.

● **¿Les dice el problema con exactitud cuántos pescados pescó Frank?** *No* **¿Polly?** *No* **¿Herman?** *Sí* **Lo que pescó Herman está al final del problema. Parece que tendremos que trabajar hacia atrás, empezamos por el final del problema y seguimos hacia el principio.**

El dibujito en la parte de arriba de la página significa que pueden trabajar hacia atrás para resolver este problema. Usaremos objetos que podamos mover de un lado a otro.

Ask whether the children ever work backwards in their daily lives. For example, if they have to be in bed at a certain time, then when do they have to start getting ready?

Use counters in the boxes to show the fish.

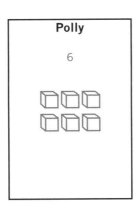

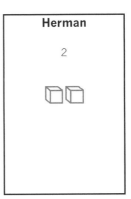

Frank	Polly	Herman
11	6	2

A. **How many fish did Herman catch?** *2* **Put 2 counters in Herman's box.**

B. **What does the problem say about how many fish Polly caught?** *She caught 4 more than Herman.* ● *Ella pescó 4 más que Herman.* **How many counters must we use for Polly's fish?** *4 more than 2; 6* ● *4 más que 2; 6* If any children suggest 4 counters, have them place the 4 counters beside Herman's counters to see if 4 is 4 more than 2. **Put 6 counters in Polly's box.**

C. **What does the problem say about how many fish Frank caught?** *He caught 5 more than Polly.* ● *Él pescó 5 más que Polly.* **If Polly caught 6 fish, how many cubes must we use for Frank's fish?** *11* **Put 11 counters in Frank's box.**

D. **Now write the number of fish in each box. How many fish did Frank catch?**

Solution: *11 fish* ● *11 pescados*

Let's look back at the problem to see if your answer fits with what the problem tells you and asks you to find. Listen to the problem again. Read the problem. **Does your answer fit?**

EXTENSION PROBLEM

How many fish did Frank catch if Herman caught 5? *14*

● **¿Cuántos pescados pescaría Frank si Herman pescara 5?** *14*

TALK ABOUT IT

Ask questions like, **How did working backwards help you solve the problem?** ● **¿Les fue de ayuda trabajar hacia atrás para resolver el problema?**

PRACTICE

Similar Practice Problem: 73

Work Backwards
Trabajar hacia atrás

Content Strands:
Number and Operations, Algebra

Each child will need 25 counters.

44

Winter is coming. It's time for the chipmunks to hunt for berries. They will put the berries into their storehouse for winter. Lisa found 5 more berries than Jared did today. Jared found 6 more berries than Tim did. Tim stopped to play, so he brought home just 2 berries. How many berries did Lisa find?

1 FIND OUT

A. **What question do you have to answer to solve the problem?** *How many berries did Lisa find?* ● *¿Cuántas bayas encontró Lisa?*

B. **What did Jared and Tim and Lisa do?** *They hunted for berries.* ● *Ellos salen a buscar bayas.* **Why?** *Winter was coming and they had to put berries into their storehouse.* ● *Se acerca el invierno y ellos tienen que guardar sus bayas en sus casas.*

C. **What do you know about how many berries Lisa found?** *She found 5 more berries than Jared did.* ● *Ella encontró 5 bayas más que Jared.* **What do you have to know before you can find out how many berries Lisa found?** *How many berries Jared found* ● *Cuantas bayas encontró Jared*

D. **What do you know about how many berries Jared found?** *He found 6 more berries than Tim did.* ● *Él encontró 6 bayas más que Tim.* **What do you have to know before you can find out how many berries Jared found?** *How many berries Tim found* ● *Cúantas bayas encontró Tim*

E. **How many berries did Tim get?** *2*

2 CHOOSE A STRATEGY

Does the problem tell us the number of berries Lisa found? *No* **Jared?** *No* **Tim?** *Yes* **Tim's number came at the end of the problem. It looks like we'll have to work backwards from the end of the problem to the beginning.**

The little picture at the top of your paper means that working backwards will help us solve this problem. We will use things that we can count, too.

● **¿Les dice el problema cuánto cuántas bayas encontró Lisa?** *No* **¿Las que encontró Jared?** *No* **¿Las que Tim?** *Sí* **La cantidad que encontró Tim está al final del problema. Parece que tendrán que empezar a trabajar desde el el final del problema hacia el comienzo del problema.**

El dibujito en la parte de arriba de la página significa que pueden trabajar hacia atrás para resolver este problema. También puede ser de ayuda usar cosas que podamos contar.

③ SOLVE IT

Tim

Jared

Lisa

TEACHING TIP

You may want to use this problem to explore equation-writing with the class. Ask the children to use the second clue to write an equation that describes how many berries Jared got. They might write Tim + 6 = Jared, or 2 + 6 = 8.

Use counters in the boxes to show the berries.

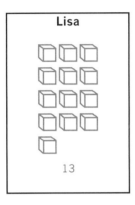

Lisa

13

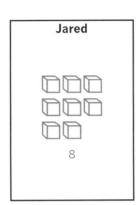

Jared

8

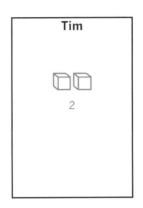

Tim

2

A. **How many berries did Tim get?** *2* **Put 2 counters in Tim's box.**

B. **What does the problem say about how many berries Jared found?** *He found 6 more than Tim did.* ● *Él encontró 6 bayas más que Tim.* **How many counters must we put in Jared's box?** *8*

C. **What does the problem say about how many berries Lisa found?** *She found 5 more than Jared did.* ● *Ella encontró 5 bayas más que Jared.* **How many counters must we put in Lisa's box?** *13*

D. **Now write the number of berries in each box. How many berries did Lisa find?**

Solution: *13 berries* ● *13 bayas*

④ LOOK BACK

Let's look back at the problem to see if your answer fits with what the problem tells you and asks you to find. Listen to the problem again. Read the problem. **Does your answer fit?**

EXTENSION PROBLEM

How many berries did Lisa bring home if Tim found 5 berries? *16*

● ¿Cuántas bayas lleva Lisa a casa si Tim lleva 5 bayas? *16*

TALK ABOUT IT

Ask questions like, **Can you use the counters and boxes again to solve this problem? Can you think of another way?** ● ¿Pueden volver a usar las fichas y las cajas para resolver este problema? ¿Pueden resolver el problema de otra manera?

PRACTICE

Similar Practice Problem: 73

Work Backwards
Trabajar hacia atrás

 Each child will need 20 counters.

45

Seth, Larry, and Todd are collecting Goofy Gumbo cards. Seth has the most cards. He has 7 more cards than Larry has. Larry has 5 more cards than Todd has. Sometimes Todd forgets where he puts his cards, so he only has 3. How many cards does Seth have?

1 FIND OUT

A. **What question do you have to answer to solve the problem?** *How many cards does Seth have?* ● *¿Cuántas tarjetas tiene Seth?*

B. **What are Seth, Larry, and Todd collecting?** *Goofy Gumbo cards* ● *Tarjetas Goofy Gumbo*

C. **Who has the most cards?** *Seth* **What do you know about how many cards Seth has?** *He has 7 more than Larry has.* ● *Seth tiene 7 tarjetas más que Larry.*

D. **What do you know about how many cards Larry has?** *He has 5 more than Todd has.* ● *Larry tiene 5 más que Todd.*

E. **How many cards does Todd have?** *3*

2 CHOOSE A STRATEGY

Does the problem tell us the number of cards Seth has? *No* **Larry?** *No* **Todd?** *Yes* **What does the little picture at the top of your paper mean?** *Working backwards will help us solve this problem.*

What else can you use to help you solve the problem? *Things that we can count*

● **¿Qué significa el dibujito en la parte de arriba de la página?** *Significa que podemos trabajar hacia atrás para resolver este problema.*

¿Qué otra cosa pueden usar para resolver el problema? *Cosas que podamos contar*

③ SOLVE IT

Larry   Todd   Seth

Use counters in the boxes to show the cards.

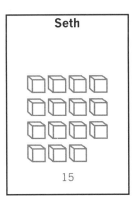

Seth

15

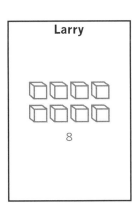

Larry

8

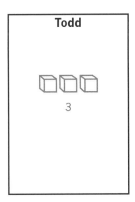

Todd

3

A. **How many cards does Todd have?** *3* **Put 3 counters in Todd's box.**

B. **How many cards does Larry have?** *5 more than Todd* ● *5 más que Todd* **How many counters must we use for Larry's cards?** *8*

C. **How many cards does Seth have?** *7 more than Larry* ● *7 más que Larry* **If Larry has 8 cards, how many counters must we use for Seth's cards?** *15*

D. **How must you show the answer?** *Write the number.* ● *Escriban la cantidad.* **How many cards does Seth have?**

Solution: *15 cards* ● *15 tarjetas*

④ LOOK BACK

Let's look back at the problem to see if your answer fits with what the problem tells you and asks you to find. Listen to the problem again. Read the problem. **Does your answer fit?**

EXTENSION PROBLEM

How many cards does Seth have if Todd has 5? *17*
● **¿Cuántas tarjetas tendría Seth si Todd tuviera 5?** *17*

TALK ABOUT IT

Ask questions like, **How could you use the counters and boxes to solve this problem?**
● **¿Cómo pueden usar las fichas y las cajas para resolver este problema?**

PRACTICE

Similar Practice Problem: 73

Use or Make a Picture or Diagram
Usar o hacer un dibujo o un diagrama

Content Strands:
Number and Operations, Algebra,
Geometry

 Each child will need 6 different colors of crayons.

46 Cheery Mouse lives in an old tree trunk. Cheery can choose from 2 tunnels to get into her house. Both tunnels go to Cheery's living room. Then there are 3 tunnels that go from the living room to her kitchen. Cheery goes to her kitchen as soon as she comes home. She likes to take a different path every time. What are the 6 different paths Cheery can take from the outside to her kitchen?

❶ FIND OUT

A. **What question do you have to answer to solve the problem?** *What are the 6 different paths Cheery can take from the outside to her kitchen?* ● *¿Cuáles son los 6 caminos que Cheery puede tomar desde afuera hasta la cocina de su casa?*

B. **Where is Cheery's home?** *In an old tree trunk* ● *En el tronco de un viejo árbol*

C. **What does Cheery do as soon as she comes home?** *She goes to her kitchen.* ● *Va a la cocina.* **What does Cheery like to do differently each day?** *Take different paths to her kitchen* ● *Toma diferentes caminos para llegar a la cocina.* **What is a path?** *A way to get from one place to another* ● *Una manera de ir de un lugar a otro*

D. **How many tunnels can Cheery go through to get into her house?** *2* **Which room do both of those tunnels lead to?** *The living room* ● *A la sala* **How many tunnels can Cheery go through to get from her living room to her kitchen?** *3*

TEACHING TIP

Have the children show different paths from the classroom door to the far side of the room. Stress that paths can be different even if they start in the same way.

---

❷ CHOOSE A STRATEGY

Would it help us solve the problem if we could "see" Cheery coming in from outside and going through the tunnels to her kitchen? *Yes*

The little picture at the top of your paper means that you can use or make a picture to help you solve the problem. Let's use the picture on your paper. We'll trace the paths in different colors. How many different crayons will we need? *6*

● **¿Les ayudaría a resolver el problema si pudieran "ver" a Cheery ir desde afuera y pasar por los túneles hasta la cocina?** *Sí*

El dibujito en la parte de arriba de la página significa que pueden usar o hacer un dibujo para resolver este problema. Usemos los dibujos en el cuaderno de trabajo. Colorearemos los caminos de diferentes colores. ¿Cuántos creyones se necesitarán? *6*

3 SOLVE IT

A. **How many tunnels can Cheery take from outside to her living room?** *2* **Cheery passes an ant in one tunnel, so we'll call that one "ant tunnel." What shall we call the other tunnel?** *Basket tunnel* ● *El túnel canasta*

B. **How many tunnels can Cheery take from her living room to the kitchen?** *3* **What names can we give to the tunnels?** *Chair, drum, and egg* ● *Silla, tambor y huevo*

C. **Let's start with the ant tunnel. Move your crayon through the ant tunnel into the living room. Which tunnel can Cheery take from her living room to her kitchen?** *Chair, drum, or egg* ● *Silla, tambor o huevo* **Move your crayon through the chair tunnel first. You have traced one path.**

D. **Take a different crayon to trace a different path. Can you start with the ant tunnel and still find a different path?** Help the children see that a path beginning with the ant tunnel again can be a different path. **Move your crayon through the ant tunnel to the living room and through the drum tunnel to the kitchen. That is a second path.**

E. Continue in the same way until the children have traced the three different paths that begin with the ant tunnel and the three different paths that begin with the basket tunnel.

Solution: See the picture.

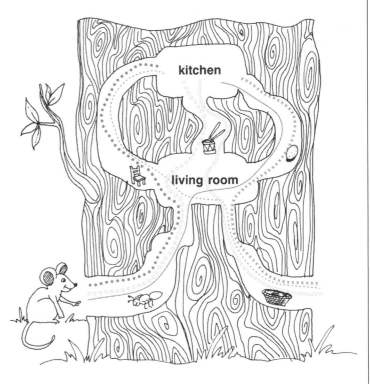

4 LOOK BACK

Let's look back at the problem to see if your answer fits with what the problem tells you and asks you to find. Listen to the problem again. Read the problem. **Does your answer fit?**

EXTENSION PROBLEM

How many different paths could Cheery take if the egg tunnel got filled up with dirt and she couldn't use it? *4*

● **¿Cuántos caminos puede tomar Cheery si el túnel huevo se llenara de tierra y ella no lo pudiera usar?** *4*

TALK ABOUT IT

Ask questions like, **How did you use the picture to solve this problem?** ● **¿Les fue de ayudar usar los dibujos para resolver el problema?**

PRACTICE

Similar Practice Problem: 74

Use or Make a Picture or Diagram
Usar o hacer un dibujo o un diagrama

Content Strands:
Number and Operations, Algebra, Geometry

 Each child will need 6 different colors of crayons.

47

Gregory Groundhog lives in a cozy home under the ground. Gregory has 3 holes that lead underground. Each hole takes Gregory into a big tunnel that has 2 doors. Gregory can go through either door to get into his home. What are the 6 different paths Gregory can take from above the ground down into his home?

1 FIND OUT

A. **What question do you have to answer to solve the problem?** *What are the 6 different paths that Gregory can take from above the ground down into his home?* ●*¿Cuáles son los 6 caminos que Gregory puede tomar desde la superficie hasta su casa subterránea?*

B. **Where is Gregory's home?** *Underground* ●*Bajo la tierra*

C. **How many holes can Gregory choose from to go into the ground to the big tunnel?** *3*

D. **How many doors can Gregory choose from to go from the big tunnel into his home?** *2*

2 CHOOSE A STRATEGY

Would it help us solve the problem if we could "see" Gregory coming from above the ground and going down through the holes and tunnel doors to his home? *Yes*

The little picture at the top of your paper means that you can use a picture to help you solve the problem. You can use the picture on your paper and crayons to mark the different paths in different colors. How many different crayons will you need? *6*

● ¿Les ayudaría a resolver el problema si pudieran "ver" a Gregory ir desde la superficie, pasar por los huecos, ir por el túnel y pasar por las puertas hasta entrar a su casa? *Sí*

El dibujito en la parte de arriba de la página significa que pueden usar un dibujo para resolver este problema. Pueden usar el dibujo en los cuadernos de trabajo y los creyones para marcar los caminos con diferentes colores. ¿Cuántos creyones necesitarán? *6*

TEACHING TIP

Ask the children how many paths they can think of to get from their classroom to another place in the school. Have them use "landmarks" to describe each path.

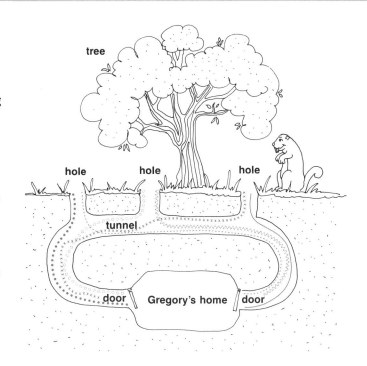

3 SOLVE IT

A. **How many holes can Gregory take from above ground to the tunnel?** *3* **Let's give them numbers. Write *1* next to one hole, *2* next to another hole, and *3* next to the third hole.**

B. **How many doors can Gregory take from the big tunnel into his home?** *2* The children can mark the doors A and B.

C. **Let's start with hole 1. Move a crayon through the hole and into the tunnel. Keep moving the crayon through one of the doors into Gregory's home. That's one path. Can Gregory start at hole 1 again and take another path to his home?** *Yes, through the other tunnel door* ● *Sí, por la otra puerta del túnel* **Trace that path with a different crayon.**

D. **Now start at hole 2. How many paths can you find?** *2* **Trace them with different crayons.**

E. **Now start at hole 3. How many paths can you find?** *2* **Trace them with different crayons.**

Solution: See the picture.

4 LOOK BACK

Let's look back at the problem to see if your answer fits with what the problem tells you and asks you to find. Listen to the problem again. Read the problem. **Does your answer fit?**

EXTENSION PROBLEM

How many different paths could Gregory take if one of the doors was locked? *3* **What if both doors were unlocked, but one of the holes was blocked?** *4*

● **¿Cuántos caminos puede tomar Gregory si una de las puertas estuviera cerrada con llave?** *3* **¿Y si las dos puertas estuvieran sin llave, pero se hubiera cerrado un hueco?** *4*

TALK ABOUT IT

Ask questions like, **How can you change the picture to help you solve the problem?** ● **¿Cómo pueden cambiar el dibujo para a resolver este problema?**

PRACTICE

Similar Practice Problem: 74

Use or Make a Picture or Diagram
Usar o hacer un dibujo o un diagrama

 Each child will need crayons.

48

Mr. Small loves his little house. He has a special room with a desk where he likes to work. There are two doors to his house from outside. Inside, there are 3 different entrances to the room with his desk. Mr. Small likes to take a different path to his desk each time he comes in. What are all the different paths Mr. Small can take from outside his house to his desk?

1 FIND OUT

A. **What question do you have to answer to solve the problem?** *What are all the different paths Mr. Small can take from outside his house to his desk?* ● *¿Cuáles son los caminos que puede tomar el señor Small desde afuera de la casa hasta su escritorio?*

B. **Where does Mr. Small like to work?** *In a special room with a desk in his house* ● *En una habitación especial donde tiene un escritorio*

C. **How many doors can Mr. Small choose from to go into his house?** *2*

D. **How many entrances can Mr. Small choose from to go into the room with his desk?** *3*

2 CHOOSE A STRATEGY

What does the little picture at the top of your paper mean? *We can use or make a picture to help us solve the problem.* **Use the picture on your paper.**

The problem tells you to trace the paths with different colors. Does the problem tell you how many different crayons you will need? *No*

● **¿Qué significa el dibujito en la parte de arriba de la página?** *Significa que puedemos usar o hacer un dibujo para resolver este problema.* **Usen los dibujos en los cuadernos de trabajo.**

El problema pide que coloreen los caminos de diferentes colores. ¿Les dice el problema cuántos creyones de diferentes colores necesitarán? *No*

3 SOLVE IT

A. **How many doors can Mr. Small go through to get into the house?** *2* **How many entrances can he use to get into the room with his desk?** *3* **Have the children label the doors and entrances.**

B. **Let's start with one door. Move a crayon through that door, through a hallway, and up to one of the entrances to the room with his desk. Keep moving the crayon until it reaches Mr. Small's desk. That's one path. Can Mr. Small start at the same door and still take another path to his desk?** *Yes, he can use different hallways to reach another entrance.* ● *Sí, él puede usar diferentes pasillos para entrar por otra puerta.* **Trace that path with a different crayon. Can Mr. Small start at the same door and take a third path to his desk?** *Yes, through different hallways to another entrance* ● *Sí, por diferentes pasillos para entrar por otra puerta.* **Are there any more ways to Mr. Small's desk through that same door?** *No*

C. **Now start at the second door. How many paths can you find?** *3* **Trace them with different crayons.**

D. **Count the different colors of paths on your paper. How many different paths can Mr. Small take?** *6*

Solution: See the picture.

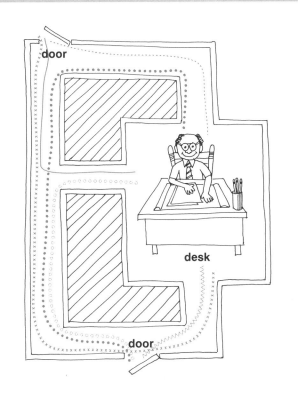

4 LOOK BACK

Let's look back at the problem to see if your answer fits with what the problem tells you and asks you to find. Listen to the problem again. Read the problem. **Does your answer fit?**

EXTENSION PROBLEM

How many different paths could Mr. Small take if one of the entrances to the little room was blocked? *4*

● **¿Cuántos caminos puede tomar el señor Small si una de las puertas de entrada a donde está su escritorio estuviera cerrada?** *4*

TALK ABOUT IT

Ask questions like, **Which entrance did you block off to solve this problem?** ● **¿Cuál entrada cerraron para resolver el problema?**

PRACTICE

Similar Practice Problem: 74

Make It Simpler
Simplificar

Have string (or ribbon) and scissors available.

49

Ann, Betsy, Carol, and Dee are taking swimming lessons at the park. They are getting ready to give a show. One part of the show is very pretty. The girls hold colored ribbons and float in the water. Each girl is joined to each of the other girls by a ribbon. How many ribbons do the girls need?

1 FIND OUT

A. **What question do you have to answer to solve the problem?** *How many ribbons do the girls need?* ●*¿Cuántas cintas necesitan las niñas?*

B. **How many swimmers are there?** *4* **What are their names?** *Ann, Betsy, Carol, Dee* **What are they doing?** *Getting ready to put on a swim show* ●*Ellas se están preparando para hacer un espectáculo ante el público.*

C. **What do the girls do in one part of the show?** *Hold colored ribbons and float in the water* ●*Ellas sostienen cintas y flotadores de colores en el agua.*

D. **What does "joined" mean?** *Connected* ●*Unidas* **What connects the girls?** *Ribbon* ●*Cintas* **If each girl is joined to each other girl, which girls will Ann be connected to?** *Betsy, Carol, Dee* **Which girls will Betsy be connected to?** *Ann, Carol, Dee*

2 CHOOSE A STRATEGY

The little picture at the top of your paper means that we can make the problem simpler, or easier, to help us solve it. We'll make the problem easier by starting with 2 swimmers instead of all 4. We'll find out how many ribbons are needed for 2 swimmers. Then we'll find out how many ribbons are needed for 3 swimmers, and then 4. We will act out the problem, too.

● El dibujito en la parte de arriba de la página significa que pueden simplificar o hacer más sencillo el problema para resolverlo. Simplificaremos el problema empezando con 2 nadadoras en vez de 4. Hallaremos cuántas cintas se necesitan para 2 nadadoras. Después hallaremos cuántas cintas se necesitan para 3 nadadoras y después para 4. Representar el problema también puede ayudar a resolverlo.

TEACHING TIP
Suggest that as the children in front act out the problem, the rest of the children may draw lines (ribbons) on the picture on their papers to record what is happening between the swimmers. This will help them develop a concrete strategy for thinking about similar problems in the future.

---

❸ SOLVE IT

Look at the table that has been started.

A. Have 2 children begin to act out the problem as Ann and Betsy. Give them one piece of string or ribbon. **How many ribbons are needed to join Ann to Betsy?** *1* **Do we need another ribbon to join Betsy to Ann?** *No* **How many ribbons in all are needed to join 2 swimmers?** *1*

B. Have a third child join the actors as Carol. Provide extra string as needed. **How many ribbons are needed to join Ann with Carol?** *1* **Is another ribbon needed to join Carol with Ann?** *No* **Must anyone else in this group be joined with a ribbon?** *Betsy and Carol* ● *Betsy y Carol* **How many ribbons are needed to join them?** *1* **How many ribbons are needed in all to join 3 swimmers?** *3*

C. **Let's fill in the number table on your paper. How many ribbons are needed for 2 swimmers?** *1* **For 3 swimmers?** *3*

D. Have a fourth child act as Dee. Let the children guide you to provide the necessary ribbons to connect Dee with the other actors. Then have each actor hold up the ends of the 3 ribbons he or she is holding to verify that each actor is joined to each other actor by a ribbon. Have the children complete the table. **How many ribbons are needed to join 4 swimmers?** *6*

Solution: *6 ribbons* ● *6 cintas*

How many ribbons do the girls need if

2 swimmers are swimming in the show? ____1____

3 swimmers are swimming in the show? ____3____

4 swimmers are swimming in the show? ____6____

❹ LOOK BACK

Let's look back at the problem to see if your answer fits with what the problem tells you and asks you to find. Listen to the problem again. Read the problem. **Does your answer fit?**

EXTENSION PROBLEM

How many ribbons are needed for 5 swimmers? *10*

● **¿Cuántas cintas se necesitan para 5 nadadoras?** *10*

TALK ABOUT IT

Ask questions like, **How did you make sure each swimmer was connected to each other swimmer? Do you see a pattern in your table? Could you use it to predict the number of ribbons needed for 6 swimmers?** ● **¿Cómo aseguraron de que cada nadadora se mantuviera unida con la siguiente nadadora? ¿Hay un patrón en la tabla? ¿Pueden usar el patrón para predecir la cantidad de cintas que necesitarán 6 nadadoras?**

PRACTICE

Similar Practice Problem: 75

Make It Simpler
Simplificar

50

Milo, June, Andrew, and Joan meet at the park on Saturday mornings. When they meet, each friend slaps hands with each of the other friends. How many slaps are there in all when the friends meet?

1 FIND OUT

A. **What question do you have to answer to solve the problem?** *How many slaps are there in all when the friends meet?* ● *¿Cuántas veces chocan las manos cuando los amigos se juntan?*

B. **How many friends are there?** *4* **What are their names?** *Milo, June, Andrew, Joan*

C. **What do they do on Saturday mornings?** *Meet each other at the park* ● *Los chicos se juntan en el parque.* **What do they do when they meet?** *Slap hands* ● *Chocan las manos.*

D. **Each person slaps hands with each other person. Who will Milo slap hands with?** *June, Andrew, Joan* **Who will June slap hands with?** *Milo, Andrew, Joan* **Who will Andrew slap hands with?** *Milo, June, Joan* **Who will Joan slap hands with?** *Milo, June, Andrew* **When Milo slaps hands with June, is June slapping hands with Milo at the same time?** *Yes* ● *Sí* **Then we'll count that as one slap, not two.**

2 CHOOSE A STRATEGY

The little picture at the top of your paper means that we can make the problem simpler, or easier, to help us solve it. We'll make the problem easier by starting with 2 children instead of all 4. We'll find out how many slaps there are when 2 friends meet. Then we'll find out how many slaps there are when 3 friends meet. We will act out the problem, too.

● El dibujito en la parte de arriba de la página significa que pueden simplificar o hacer más sencillo el problema para resolverlo. Simplificaremos el problema empezando con 2 amigos en vez de los 4. Hallaremos cuántas veces chocan las manos cuando dos amigos se juntan. Después hallaremos cuántas veces chocan las manos cuando 3 amigos se juntan. Actuar el problema también puede ayudar a resolverlo.

TEACHING TIP

Suggest that as the children in front act out the problem, the rest of the children may draw lines on the picture on their papers to record what is happening between the hand-slapping friends.

---

③ SOLVE IT

Look at the table that has been started.

How many slaps are there if

2 friends meet at the park? _____1_____

3 friends meet at the park? _____3_____

4 friends meet at the park? _____6_____

A. Have 2 children begin to act out the problem as Milo and June. Have them slap their hands together as shown on their papers. **How many slaps are made when 2 friends meet?** *1*

B. Have a third child join the actors as Andrew. **Let's act out what happens when 3 friends meet.** You may want to organize the acting by having Milo make all his slaps first, and then step aside, and so on. **How many slaps are made when 3 friends meet?** *3*

C. **Let's fill in the number table on your paper. How many slaps are made when 2 friends meet?** *1* **When 3 friends meet?** *3*

D. Have a fourth child join the actors as Joan. Let the children act out all the slaps. **How many hand slaps are made when 4 friends meet?** *6*

Solution: *6 hand slaps* ● *6 veces chocan las manos*

④ LOOK BACK

Let's look back at the problem to see if your answer fits with what the problem tells you and asks you to find. Listen to the problem again. Read the problem. **Does your answer fit?**

EXTENSION PROBLEM

Look for a pattern in the number table. Use the pattern to find out how many hand slaps there are when 6 friends meet. *15*

● **Busquen un patrón en la tabla. Usen el patrón para hallar las veces que chocan las manos cada vez que los 6 amigos se juntan.** *15*

TALK ABOUT IT

Ask questions like, **Can you find a way to describe the pattern in the number table so that you could make someone else understand?** ● **¿Pueden hallar una forma para describirle a otra persona el patrón que hay en la tabla?**

PRACTICE

Similar Practice Problem: 75

Make It Simpler
Simplificar

51

Marty, Gino, Heather, Latanya, and Pam are in Mr. Mustard's class. They are having a checkers tournament. Mr. Mustard asked everyone to play each of the other children once. Then the person who had won the most games would be the checker champion. So each child played each other child in one game. How many different games of checkers were played all together?

1 FIND OUT

A. **What question do you have to answer to solve the problem?** *How many different games of checkers were played all together?*
  ● *¿Cuántos partidos de damas jugaron en total?*

B. **How many children are in Mr. Mustard's class?** *5* **What are their names?** *Marty, Gino, Heather, Latanya, Pam*

C. **What are the children doing?** *Having a checkers tournament* ● *Van a participar en una competencia de damas.*

D. **What did Mr. Mustard mean when he asked everyone to play each of the other children once?** *Each child should play a game of checkers with each other child in the group.*
  ● *Los niños deben jugar un partido de damas con cada uno de los otros niños del grupo.*
  Who did Marty play checkers with? *Gino, Heather, Latanya, Pam* **Who did Gino play checkers with?** *Marty, Heather, Latanya, Pam* **Marty played with Gino, and Gino played with Marty. Is that 1 game or 2?** *1*

2 CHOOSE A STRATEGY

What does the little picture at the top of your paper mean? *We can make the problem easier to help us solve it.* **How will you make it easier?** *Start with 2 children instead of 5, and act it out.*

● **¿Qué significa el dibujito en la parte de arriba de la página?** *Significa que podemos simplificar el problema para resolverlo.* **¿Cómo pueden simplificarlo?** *Empezaremos con 2 niños en vez de 5 y actuaremos el problema.*

TEACHING TIP

Suggest that as the children in front act out the problem, the rest of the children may draw lines on the picture on their papers to record what is happening between the players.

③ SOLVE IT

Look at the table that has been started.

How many different games are there if

2 children are in the tournament? ___1___

3 children are in the tournament? ___3___

4 children are in the tournament? ___6___

5 children are in the tournament? ___10___

A. Have 2 children begin to act out the problem. **How many different checker games will there be if Marty and Gino are the only children in the tournament?** *1*

B. Have a third child join the actors as Heather. Have the children model the three different ways of pairing up. **How many different checker games will there be in all if Heather joins Marty and Gino?** *3*

C. **Fill in the number table on your paper. How many different pairs will there be with 2 children?** *1* **With 3 children?** *3* Have a fourth child join the actors. Let them act out all possible pairings. Help the children keep track of the different pairs. **How many different games will there be if 4 children are in the tournament?** *6*

D. Have a fifth child join the actors. As they act out all possible pairings, have the children keep track of the different pairs. **How many different games of checkers were played all together?**

Solution: *10 games* ● *10 partidos*

④ LOOK BACK

Let's look back at the problem to see if your answer fits with what the problem tells you and asks you to find. Listen to the problem again. Read the problem. **Does your answer fit?**

EXTENSION PROBLEM

Look for a pattern in the number table. Use the pattern to find out how many different pairs of children there would be if 6 children were in the checker tournament. *15*

● **Mira el patrón que está en la tabla. Usa el patrón para hallar cuántos pares de niños tendrían si fueran 6 niños los que participan en la competencia de damas.** *15*

TALK ABOUT IT

Ask questions like, **Does the number of games go up in the same way each time a new player is added?** ● **¿Aumenta la cantidad de partidos de la misma manera cada vez que se suma un nuevo jugador?**

PRACTICE

Similar Practice Problem: 75

Brainstorm
Generar ideas

 Each child may need 3 counters.

52

Fiona is giving you a puzzle to solve. She says, "There are 2 circles on the floor. One circle is large. The other circle is small. There are 3 lions in the large circle. There are 2 lions in the small circle. But there are only 3 lions in all. Where is the small circle, and where are the lions?"

1 FIND OUT

A. **What question do you have to answer to solve the problem?** *Where is the small circle, and where are the lions?* ● *¿Dónde está el círculo pequeño y dónde están los leones?*

B. **In Fiona's puzzle, how many circles are on the floor?** 2 **What sizes are they?** *One large, one small* ● *Uno grande y uno pequeño*

C. **What is inside the large circle?** *3 lions* ●*3 leones* **What is inside the small circle?** *2 lions* ●*2 leones*

D. **How many lions are there in all?** *3 lions* ●*3 leones*

2 CHOOSE A STRATEGY

Before you explain why brainstorming is a good strategy for solving this problem, you may want to model a few incorrect solutions to help the children see that the problem doesn't give any clues to the correct solution.

The little picture at the top of your paper means that we can use a special kind of thinking called "brainstorming" to solve this problem. When you brainstorm, you think about things in new ways.

It may help us to use counters, too. We can pretend the counters are the lions. We can move them around until we find the answer.

● El dibujito en la parte de arriba de la página significa que podemos usar una estrategia especial llamada "generar ideas" para resolver este problema. Cuando generan ideas, piensan en diferentes maneras que las que normalmente pensarían acerca de las cosas.

También podemos usar fichas para contar. Podemos imaginar que las fichas son los leones. Podemos moverlos de un lado a otro hasta que hallemos la respuesta.

3 SOLVE IT

TEACHING TIP

You may want to make an overhead transparency of the lion picture and provide a piece of string. Allow children to come up and make a circle with the string to show where they believe the small circle should go. Have the class decide whether that position satisfies the conditions of the problem.

A. **What do you know about the circles?** *There are 2 of them; they are on the floor; one is small; one is large* ● *Que hay dos; que están en el suelo; que uno es pequeño; que otro es grande* **Look at the picture on your paper. Which circle is shown in the picture?** *The large circle*
● *El círculo grande*

B. **What do you know about the lions?** *There are 3 lions in the large circle; there are 2 lions in the small circle; there are 3 lions in all.* ● *Que hay 3 leones en el círculo grande; que hay 2 leones en el círculo pequeño; que en total hay 3 leones* **How many lions are there in all?** *3* **So how many counters shall we use?** *3*

C. **How many counters shall we put in the large circle?** *3* **How many will we need to put in the small circle?** *2* **Do we have any counters left over to put in the small circle?** *No*

D. **Does anyone have any ideas about where we should put the small circle?** Allow the children to play with ideas until someone suggests that you put the small circle partially or totally inside the large circle. **Draw the small circle to show where the lions are in the circles.**

4 LOOK BACK

Solution: See the picture.

Let's look back at the problem to see if your answer fits with what the problem tells you and asks you to find. Listen to the problem again. Read the problem. **Does your answer fit?**

EXTENSION PROBLEM

What might the circles and lions look like if there were 3 lions in the large circle, 2 lions in the small circle, and 4 lions in all? Draw the circles and the lions.

● **¿Cómo se verían los círculos y los leones si hubiera 3 leones en el círculo grande, 2 leones en el círculo pequeño y 4 leones en total? Dibujen los círculos y los leones.**

Answers will vary; the circles must overlap, with 1 of the lions in both circles, or the children may reuse the solution to the original problem and place 1 lion outside the circles, since the problem doesn't specify that each lion must be in a circle.

TALK ABOUT IT

Ask questions like, **Did you put one of the circles in a different place? Where did you place the 4th lion? Were all four lions included in at least one of the circles?** ● **¿Pusieron uno de los círculos en un lugar diferente? ¿Dónde pusieron el 4º león? ¿Pusieron los cuatro leones en por lo menos uno de los círculos?**

PRACTICE

Similar Practice Problem: 76

Brainstorm
Generar ideas

Content Strand:
Geometry

 Each child will need 6 counters.

53

Look at this group of 6 baby chicks. It looks like a triangle pointing up to the top of the page.

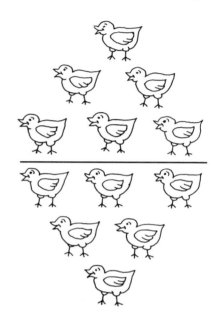

Now look at the chicks again. Only 2 chicks have moved. But now the group looks like a triangle pointing down to the bottom of the page. Which 2 chicks moved?

1 FIND OUT

A. **What question do you have to answer to solve the problem?** *Which 2 chicks moved?* ● *¿Cuáles son los 2 pollitos que se movieron?*

B. **How many baby chicks are in the group?** *6*

C. **What shape was made by the group of chicks?** *A triangle* ● *Un triángulo* **In which direction did the first triangle point?** *Up* ● *Arriba*

D. **What happened when 2 chicks moved?** *The triangle changed; now it points down.* ● *El triángulo cambió; ahora señala hacia abajo.*

2 CHOOSE A STRATEGY

This problem is a puzzle. It doesn't give us many clues. What can we do to help us solve the problem? *We can brainstorm.* When you brainstorm, you think about things in new ways.

We can use counters, too. We can pretend the counters are the chicks.

● Este problema es una adivinanza. No da muchas pistas. ¿Qué podemos hacer para resolver el problema? *Podemos generar ideas.* Cuando generan ideas, piensan en diferentes maneras que las que normalmente pensarían acerca de las cosas.

Podemos usar fichas. Podemos imaginar que las fichas son los pollitos.

106   The Problem Solver

TEACHING TIP

Place 6 counters on an overhead projector or 6 magnets on the board in the first configuration shown in the problem. Allow children to come up and move 2 chicks at a time. Have the rest of the class determine whether the configuration each volunteer makes matches the second triangle shown in the problem. Remind children to return the chicks to the original configuration before trying each new solution.

A. **How many chicks are there in all?** *6* **So how many counters shall we use?** *6*

B. **Look at how the chicks stood to make the first triangle.** Have the children describe the configuration. **Make the same triangle with your 6 counters.**

C. **What did the chicks do next?** *They made a different triangle.* ● *Ellos hicieron un triángulo diferente.* **How many chicks moved to make the different triangle?** *2* **Try to find out which chicks moved. Remember that you may only move 2 counters to change the first triangle into the second triangle.** Allow the children to move the counters around until someone solves the problem.

D. **How must we show the answer?** *Color the 2 chicks that moved.* ● *Coloreamos los 2 pollitos que se movieron.*

Solution:

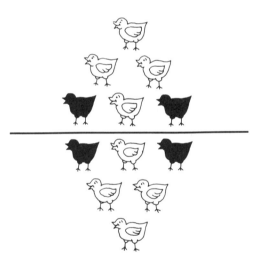

4 LOOK BACK

Let's look back at the problem to see if your answer fits with what the problem tells you and asks you to find. Listen to the problem again. Read the problem. **Does your answer fit?**

EXTENSION PROBLEM

What if the triangle that points up had a row of four chicks added at the bottom? Then there would be 10 chicks all together. How many chicks would need to move to make the triangle point down? Move as few chicks as possible. *3; the "angles" of the triangle*

● **¿Qué pasaría si al triángulo que señala hacia arriba se le añadiera una fila de cuatro pollitos en la parte de abajo? Eso daría un total de 10 pollitos. ¿Cuántos pollitos tienen que moverse para hacer que el triángulo señale hacia abajo? Muevan la menor cantidad posible de pollitos.** *3; los "ángulos" del triángulo*

TALK ABOUT IT

Ask questions like, **How was the solution to this problem similar to the solution to the original problem?** ● **¿Fue la solución de este problema similar a la solución del problema original?**

PRACTICE

Similar Practice Problem: 76

Brainstorm
Generar ideas

 Each child may need 9 counters.

54

Marne is giving you a puzzle to solve. He says, "I saw a trail of snails in my garden. There were 2 snails behind a snail and 2 snails in front of a snail. There was a snail between 2 snails, too. What is the smallest number of snails there could be in that trail?"

1 FIND OUT

A. **What question do you have to answer to solve the problem?** *What is the smallest number of snails there could be in that trail?* ● *¿Cuál es la cantidad mínima de caracoles en la fila?*

B. **What did Marne see?** *A trail of snails* ● *Una fila de caracoles* **Where?** *In his garden* ● *En el jardín*

C. **How many snails were behind another snail?** *2* **How many snails were in front of another snail?** *2* **How many snails were between 2 snails?** *1*

2 CHOOSE A STRATEGY

Allow children to suggest solutions. Encourage a variety of suggestions, and ask how each child arrived at the number he or she suggested.

What does the little picture at the top of your paper mean? *We can brainstorm to solve the problem.* **What does brainstorm mean?** *Look at things in new ways and try many different ideas.* **Let's use counters, too. Does the problem tell us how many we'll need?** *No, that's what we have to find out.*

● **¿Qué significa el dibujito en la parte de arriba de la página?** *Significa que podemos generar ideas para resolver este problema.* **¿Qué significa generar ideas?** *Ver las cosas de manera diferente y tratar de solucionarlas de manera diferente a como generalmente se haría.* **Usemos también las fichas. ¿Nos dice el problema cuántas fichas vamos a necesitar?** *No, eso es lo que tenemos que hallar.*

Use your counters and the clues.

A. **How many snails were behind another snail?** *2* Have the children start modeling the trail. **How many counters must be in the trail to fit that clue?** *At least 3* ● *Por lo menos 3*

B. **How many snails were in front of another snail?** *2* What can we do to fit this clue? Answers will vary. Allow the children to experiment with the counters and share their ideas. Challenge them to find a way to use a smaller number of snails to satisfy both clues until someone suggests that one of the snails behind a snail could also be one of the snails in front of a snail. A line of the same 3 snails satisfies the first and the second clue.

C. **How many snails were between 2 snails?** *1* **What can we do to fit this clue?** Answers will vary. Allow the children to experiment with the counters and share their ideas. Challenge them to find a way to use a smaller number of snails to satisfy all three clues until someone suggests that one of the snails in the trail of 3 is between 2 snails. The same 3 snails satisfy all three clues.

Solution: *3 snails* ● *3 caracoles*

4 **LOOK BACK**

Let's look back at the problem to see if your answer fits with what the problem tells you and asks you to find. Listen to the problem again. Read the problem. **Does your answer fit?**

EXTENSION PROBLEM

What if all the clues stayed the same except the last one? What if there were 2 snails between two other snails? What is the smallest number of snails there could be in the trail now? *4*

● **¿Qué pasaría si las pistas fueran las mismas excepto la última? ¿Qué pasaría si hay 2 caracoles en medio de dos caracoles? ¿Cuál sería la cantidad mínima de caracoles en la fila?** *4*

TALK ABOUT IT

Ask questions like, **How did you solve this problem? Did you use the same strategy as we used for the original problem?** ● **¿Qué hicieron para resolver el problema? ¿Usaron la misma estrategia que usaron para resolver el problema original?**

PRACTICE

Similar Practice Problem: 76

Use or Make a Picture or Diagram
Usar o hacer un dibujo o un diagrama

Content Strands:
Number and Operations,
Algebra, Data Analysis
and Probability

55

Mr. Hall's class voted for their favorite recess games. The graph shows how many children voted for each game.

- Sean's favorite game was the one that most of the boys liked.
- Equal numbers of boys and girls liked Rachel's favorite game.
- Two more girls than boys liked Alyssa's favorite game.

Which games do Sean, Rachel, and Alyssa like best?

① FIND OUT

A. **What question do you have to answer to solve the problem?** *Which games do Sean, Rachel, and Alyssa like best?* ● *¿Cuál es el juego favorito de Sean, Rachel y Alyssa?*

B. **What do you know about Sean's favorite game?** *It was the game most of the boys liked.* ● *Es el juego que más les gusta a los niños.*

C. **What do you know about Rachel's favorite game?** *Equal numbers of boys and girls voted for it.* ● *Igual cantidad de niños y de niñas votaron por ese juego.*

D. **What do you know about Alyssa's favorite game?** *Two more girls than boys voted for it.* ● *Dos niñas más que los niños votaron por ese juego.*

TEACHING TIP

Discuss the terms *two more than* and *equal numbers*. Have the children use these phrases to talk about boys and girls or things in the classroom. For instance, they might say *There are 3 more girls than boys at the round table*, or *There are equal numbers of red and blue shapes on the poster*.

② CHOOSE A STRATEGY

The little picture at the top of your paper means that we can use a picture or diagram to solve the problem. A graph is a kind of diagram.

● El dibujito en la parte de arriba de la página significa que podemos usar un dibujo o un diagrama para resolver este problema. Una gráfica es un tipo de diagrama.

3 SOLVE IT

Look at the graph and the clues.

A. **What can you tell by looking at this graph?** Encourage the children to talk about the graph and what it shows.

B. **What are the names on the side?** *4 types of recess games: swings, kickball, tag, and jump rope* ● *4 clases de juegos durante el receso: columpios, patear la pelota, correr y saltar la cuerda* **What pictures do you see next to the name of each game?** *The faces of boys and girls* ● *Las caras de los niños y las niñas* **What does each boy's face stand for?** *1 boy who voted* ● *Por un niño que votó* **What does each girl's face stand for?** *1 girl who voted* ● *Por una niña que votó*

C. You may want to have the children count and record the number of girls, the number of boys, and the total number of students who voted for each game.

D. **Let's start with the clue for Sean's favorite recess game. What is the clue about Sean's game?** *It was the game most of the boys liked.* ● *Fue el juego que les gustó más a los niños.* **Do we need to look at girls' votes, boys' votes, or both to find Sean's favorite game?** *Boys' votes* ● *Los votos de los niños* You may want to have the children record the numbers they find. **How many boys voted for swings?** *2* **Kickball?** *6* **Tag?** *3* **Jump rope?** *1* **Which game fits the clue for Sean?** *Kickball* ● *Patear la pelota*

E. **What is the clue for Rachel's favorite game?** *Equal numbers of boys and girls like it.* ● *Que le gusta a igual cantidad de niños y niñas* **Do we need to look at girls' votes, boys' votes, or both to find Rachel's favorite game?** *Both* ● *Ambos* **How many girls voted for swings?** *5* **Boys?** *2* **How many girls voted for kickball?** *3* **Boys?** *6* **How many girls voted for tag?** *3* **Boys?** *3* **How many girls voted for jump rope?** *3* **Boys?** *1* **Which game fits the clue for Rachel?** *Tag* ● *Correr*

F. **What is the clue about Alyssa's favorite recess activity?** *Two more girls than boys voted for it.* ● *Dos niñas más que los niños votaron por ese juego.* **Do we need to look at girls' votes, boys' votes, or both?** *Both* ● *Ambos* **Which game did 2 more girls than boys vote for?** *Jump rope* ● *Saltar la cuerda* **Which game fits the clue for Alyssa?** *Jump rope* ● *Saltar la cuerda*

Solution: *Sean—kickball, Rachel—tag, Alyssa—jump rope* ● *Sean—patear la pelota, Rachel—correr, Alyssa—saltar la cuerda*

4 LOOK BACK

Let's look back. Listen to the problem again. Read the problem. **Does your answer fit?**

Favorite Recess Games

Swings	🙂	🙂	🙂	🙂	🙂	🙂	🙂		
Kickball	🙂	🙂	🙂	🙂	🙂	🙂	🙂	🙂	🙂
Tag	🙂	🙂	🙂	🙂	🙂	🙂			
Jump Rope	🙂	🙂	🙂	🙂					

🙂 = 1 girl

🙂 = 1 boy

EXTENSION PROBLEM

Meg voted for the game that was most popular for girls. Which game does Meg like best? *Swings*

● Meg votó por el juego que más les gusta a las niñas. ¿Cuál es el juego que más le gusta a Meg? *Los columpios*

TALK ABOUT IT

Ask questions like, **How do picture graphs help you get information?** ● ¿Les fue de ayuda usar la gráfica de dibujos para hallar la información?

PRACTICE

Similar Practice Problem: 77

Use or Make a Picture or Diagram
Usar o hacer un dibujo o un diagrama

56

One day, the class made a graph to show how each child got to school.

- Isabelle used the way that got two fewer marks than *car*.
- Julian's way was the way most of the children got to school that day.
- Lauren's transportation got more marks than *bus* but fewer than *bike*.

How did Isabelle, Julian, and Lauren get to school?

1 FIND OUT

A. **What question do you have to answer to solve the problem?** *How did Isabelle, Julian, and Lauren get to school?* ●*¿Cómo llegan a la escuela Isabelle, Julian y Lauren?*

B. **What do you know about how Isabelle got to school?** *Her way got two fewer marks than car.* ●*Usa el transporte que obtuvo dos marcas menos que el carro.*

C. **What do you know about how Julian got to school?** *It was the way most children got to school.* ●*Usa el transporte que la mayoría de los niños usan para ir a la escuela.*

D. **What do you know about how Lauren got to school?** *Her way got more marks than* bus *but fewer than* bike. ●*Usa el transporte que obtuvo más marcas que el autobús pero menos marcas que la bicicleta.*

2 CHOOSE A STRATEGY

What does the little picture at the top of your paper mean? *We can use a picture or diagram to solve the problem.* **A graph is a kind of diagram.**

● **¿Qué significa el dibujito en la parte de arriba de la página?** *Significa que podemos usar un dibujo o un diagrama para resolver este problema.* **Una gráfica es un tipo de diagrama.**

TEACHING TIP

Have the children examine and share their observations about the graph. Ask how many true statements they can make about how the children in Ms. Fuentes' class got to school that day.

---

3 SOLVE IT

Look at the graph and the clues.

How We Got to School

Scooter	X	X							
Bike	X	X	X	X	X	X	X		
Bus	X	X	X						
Car	X	X	X	X	X				
Walk	X	X	X	X	X	X	X	X	X

A. **What can you tell by looking at this graph?** Encourage the children to talk about the graph and what it shows.

B. **What are the names on the side?** *5 ways of getting to school: walk, car, bus, bike, scooter* ● *5 maneras de llegar a la escuela: caminando, en carro, en autobús, en bicicleta, en patineta* **What do the Xs next to each name show?** *How many children got to school in that way* ● *Cuantos niños van a la escuela de esa manera*

C. You may want to start by having the children count the number of Xs for each way.

D. **Let's start with the clue about Isabelle. What is the clue about Isabelle's way?** *It got two fewer marks than car.* ● *Obtuvo 2 marcas menos que el carro.* **Which ways got fewer marks than car?** *Scooter and bus* ● *Patineta y autobús* **Which of those ways got exactly 2 fewer marks than car?** *Bus* ● *Autobús* **How did Isabelle get to school that day?** *By bus* ● *Autobús*

E. **Now look at the clue for Julian. What is the clue?** *It was the way most children got to school that day.* ● *Es la manera en que la mayoría de los niños llegan a la escuela.* **What will you look for to find the way that most children got to school?** *The way with the most Xs* ● *La manera que tenga la mayor cantidad de X* **Which way has the most Xs?** *Walking* ● *Caminando* **Which way fits the clue for Julian?** *Walking* ● *Caminando*

F. **What was the clue for Lauren?** *Her way got more marks than bus but fewer than bike.* ● *Obtuvo más marcas que el autobús pero menos marcas que la bicicleta.* **Which ways got more marks than bus?** *Bike, car, walk* ● *Bicicleta, carro, caminando* **Which of those ways got fewer marks than bike?** *Car* ● *Carro* **How did Lauren get to school?** *By car* ● *Carro*

Solution: *Isabelle—bus, Julian—walk, Lauren—car* ● *Isabelle—autobús, Julian—caminando, Lauren—carro*

4 LOOK BACK

Let's look back at the problem to see if your answer fits with what the problem tells you and asks you to find. Listen to the problem again. Read the problem. **Does your answer fit?**

EXTENSION PROBLEM

Eddy got to school on his scooter. Can you write a number clue to help someone look at the graph and find out which way Eddy got to school?

● **Eddy fue a la escuela en su patineta. ¿Puedes escribir una pista con número para ayudar a que una persona observe la gráfica y halle la forma en que Eddy fue a la escuela?**

Answers will vary.

TALK ABOUT IT

Ask questions like, **What comparing words could you use in your clue? How could you use more than, fewer than...?** ● **¿Cuáles palabras de comparación pueden usar en la pista? ¿Cómo pueden usar más que, más de y menos que, menos de...?**

PRACTICE

Similar Practice Problem: 77

57

There are 6 friends in the Critter Club. Each friend has a different kind of pet. For instance, John has 2 snakes, and Fiona has 1 turtle. The graph shows the kind of animal each child owns, and how many he or she has.

• Oscar has an odd number of pets.

• Ali has two more pets than John has.

• Asia's only pet just had 7 babies!

Which pets do Oscar, Ali, and Asia own?

1 FIND OUT

A. **What question do you have to answer to solve the problem?** *Which pets do Oscar, Ali, and Asia own?* ● *¿Cuáles son las mascotas de Oscar, Ali y Asia?*

B. **What do you know about Oscar's pets?** *He has an odd number.* ● *Él tiene un número impar de mascotas.*

C. **What do you know about Ali's pets?** *She has two more pets than John has.* ● *Ella tiene dos mascotas más que las que tiene John.* **How many pets does John have?** *2*

D. **What do you know about Asia's pet?** *It just had seven babies.* ● *Acaba de tener siete bebés.*

2 CHOOSE A STRATEGY

What does the little picture at the top of your paper mean? *We can use a picture or diagram to solve the problem.* **A graph is a kind of diagram.**

● **Qué significa el dibujito en la parte de arriba de la página?** *Significa que podemos usar un dibujo o diagrama para resolver este problema.* **Una gráfica es un tipo de diagrama.**

TEACHING TIP

Make sure the children understand that in this problem, the graph shows information about just six children. Each kind of pet is owned by just 1 child; the owner of the cats has 3, the owner of the birds has 4, and so on.

3 SOLVE IT

Look at the graph and the clues.

A. **What can you tell by looking at this graph?** Encourage the children to talk about the graph and what it shows.

B. **What are the names along the bottom?** *6 kinds of pets: dogs, cats, fish, turtles, birds, and snakes* ● *6 clases de mascotas: perros, gatos, peces, tortugas, aves y serpientes* **What do the Xs above each animal name show?** *The number of that kind of pet* ● *La cantidad que hay de esa mascota*

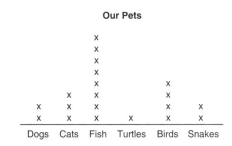

Our Pets

```
            x
            x
            x
            x
            x                 x
      x     x                 x
x     x     x                 x     x
x     x     x     x           x     x
────────────────────────────────────────
Dogs  Cats  Fish  Turtles  Birds  Snakes
```

C. **Let's start with the clue about Oscar. What is the clue?** *He has an odd number of pets.* ● *Él tiene un numero impar de mascotas.* **Which kinds of pets have an odd number of Xs?** *Turtles and cats* ● *Tortugas y gatos* **Which of those pets is matched with another person?** *Fiona owns the turtle* ● *Fiona tiene la tortuga.* **Which kind of pet does Oscar own?** *Cats* ● *Gatos* As each owner is found, have the children write the owner's name below the name of the pet. **How many cats does Oscar have?** *3*

D. **What is the clue about Ali?** *She has two more pets than John.* ● *Ella tiene dos mascotas más que las que tiene John.* **Which pet does John have?** *Snakes* ● *Serpientes* **How many does he have?** *2* **Ali has 2 more than 2 pets. How many pets does she have?** *4* **Which pet has 4 Xs?** *Birds* ● *Aves* **Which kind of pet does Ali own?** *Birds* ● *Aves* **How many does she have?** *4*

E. **What is the clue about Asia?** *Her pet just had seven babies.* ● *Su mascota acaba de tener siete bebés.* **If you count the mother and the babies, how many pets does Asia have?** *8* **Which animal has 8 Xs?** *Fish* ● *Peces* **Which kind of pet must Asia own?** *Fish* ● *Peces* **How many does she have?** *8*

Solution: *Oscar—3 cats, Ali—4 birds, Asia—8 fish*
● *Oscar—3 gatos, Ali—4 aves, Asia—8 peces*

4 LOOK BACK

Let's look back at the problem to see if your answer fits with what the problem tells you and asks you to find. Listen to the problem again. *Read the problem.* **Does your answer fit?**

EXTENSION PROBLEM

Karen has dogs. Can you write a number clue for Karen?

● **Karen tiene perros. ¿Pueden escribir una pista que diga la cantidad que tiene Karen?**

Answers will vary.

TALK ABOUT IT

Ask questions like, **Why is your clue a good one? What kind of math does it use?** ● **¿Por qué es buena la pista que dieron? ¿Qué operaciones de matemáticas usa?**

PRACTICE

Similar Practice Problem: 78

Use or Make a Picture or Diagram
Usar o hacer un dibujo o un diagrama

58

The students lined up their pencils to see whose was the longest.
Now Marta, Alex, and Nia can't remember which pencils are theirs.

• **Marta's is 1 inch longer than Ruben's.**

• **Alex's is the same length as Stella's.**

• **Nia's pencil is 2 inches longer than Ray's.**

How long are Marta, Alex, and Nia's pencils?

1 FIND OUT

A. **What question do you have to answer to solve the problem?** *How long are Marta, Alex, and Nia's pencils?* ● *¿Cuánto miden los lápices de Marta, Alex y Níá?*

B. **What do you know about Marta's pencil?** *It is 1 inch longer than Ruben's.* ● *Que mide una pulgada más que el de Rubén.*

C. **What do you know about Alex's pencil?** *It is the same length as Stella's.* ● *Que mide lo mismo que el de Stella.*

D. **What do you know about Nia's pencil?** *It is 2 inches longer than Ray's.* ● *Que mide 2 pulgadas más que el de Ray.*

2 CHOOSE A STRATEGY

What does the little picture at the top of your paper mean? *We can use a picture or diagram to solve the problem.* **A graph is a kind of diagram.**

● **¿Qué significa el dibujito en la parte de arriba de la página?** *Significa que podemos usar un dibujo o un diagrama para resolver este problema.* **Una gráfica es un tipo de diagrama.**

TEACHING TIP

Help the children become familiar with the graph. Call attention to the fact that the pencil lengths are marked along the side of the graph in 2-inch increments. The lighter lines on the graph show the odd-numbered lengths in between the labeled lengths. Ask the children to find the 6-inch, 10-inch, and 3-inch pencils.

Look at the graph and the clues.

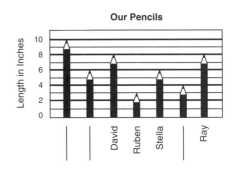

Our Pencils

A. **What can you tell by looking at this graph?** Encourage the children to talk about the graph and what it shows.

B. **What do the names along the bottom tell us?** *They tell who owns each pencil.* ● *Dicen a quién pertenecen los lápices.* **What are the blank lines for?** *The names Marta, Alex, and Nia* ● *Para los nombres Marta, Alex y Nia* **What do the numbers along the side mean?** *They tell how long the pencils are.* ● *Dicen lo que miden los lápices.* **Only the even numbers are marked. Find the mark for 2 and the mark for 4. How do you know where the mark for 3 is?** *It's the light line between 2 and 4.* ● *Es la línea clara entre el 2 y el 4.*

C. **Let's start with the clue about Marta. What is the clue?** *Her pencil is 1 inch longer than Ruben's.* ● *Su lápiz mide 1 pulgada más que el de Ruben.* **Which one is Ruben's pencil?** *The short one* ● *El más chiquito* **How long is it?** *3 inches* ● *3 pulgadas* **Can you see a pencil that is 1 inch longer than Ruben's?** *Yes, the second to the last one is 4 inches long.* ● *Sí, el penúltimo tiene 4 pulgadas de largo* **Which pencil must be Marta's?** *The 4-inch pencil* ● *El lápiz que tiene 4 pulgadas de largo.* **Let's write Marta's name on the line below that pencil.**

D. **What is the clue about Alex?** *His pencil is the same length as Stella's.* ● *Su lápiz mide lo mismo que el de Stella.* **Which pencil is Stella's?** *The one next to Marta's* ● *El que está junto al de Marta* **Can you see a pencil that is the same length as Stella's?** *Yes, the second one is also 6 inches long.* ● *Sí, el segundo también tiene 6 pulgadas de largo.* **Which pencil must be Alex's?** *The second one* ● *El segundo* **Let's write Alex's name by that pencil.**

E. **What is the clue about Nia's pencil?** *It is 2 inches longer than Ray's.* ● *Que mide 2 pulgadas más que el de Ray* **Which pencil is Ray's?** *The last one* ● *El último* **How long is Ray's pencil?** *8 inches* ● *8 pulgadas* **Which pencil must be Nia's?** *The first, which is 10 inches long* ● *El primero, el que mide 10 pulgadas de largo.* **Let's write her name by that pencil.**

Solution: *Marta's—4 inches, Alex's—6 inches, Nia's—10 inches* ● *El de Marta—4 pulgadas, el de Alex—6 pulgadas, el de Nía—10 pulgadas*

Let's look back at the problem to see if your answer fits with what the problem tells you and asks you to find. Listen to the problem again. Read the problem. **Does your answer fit?**

EXTENSION PROBLEM

What if Jesse has sharpened his pencil so often that it is shorter than Ruben's? How long might his pencil be?

● **¿Qué pasaría si porque Jesse le saca punta al lápiz muchas veces, su lápiz es más chiquito que el de Ruben? ¿Cuánto medirá entonces el lápiz de Jesse?**

Any length less than 3 inches is correct.

TALK ABOUT IT

Ask questions like, **Is there only one answer to this question? Why or why not?** ● **Hay solamente una respuesta a este problema? ¿Por qué?**

PRACTICE

Similar Practice Problem: 78

You can find these pages on the CD

NAME

59 | Practice Problem

One of these monkeys is named Noodle. You can find Noodle if you look for him.

He is hanging upside down.

He is wearing something on his head.

He has a striped shirt.

Which monkey is Noodle?

Draw a ring around Noodle.

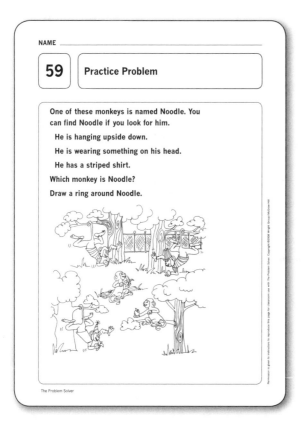

NAME

60 | Practice Problem

Mr. and Mrs. Hippo want to get new paint and a new rug for their home. The Hippo Home Store sells blue paint and yellow paint. It sells green rugs and orange rugs. Mr. and Mrs. Hippo can fix their home with new paint and a new rug. What are the 4 different ways that Mr. and Mrs. Hippo can fix their home?

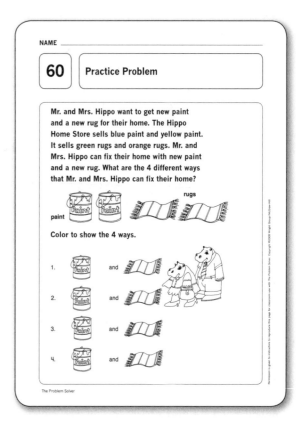

Color to show the 4 ways.

1.   and
2.   and
3.   and
4.   and

NAME

61 | Practice Problem

Helen Hen is sitting on lots of eggs in her nest. She won't tell how many! She just sits on the nest and cackles. Carmen Cat snoops around the barnyard. She found out how many eggs there are! Carmen gave you these clues.

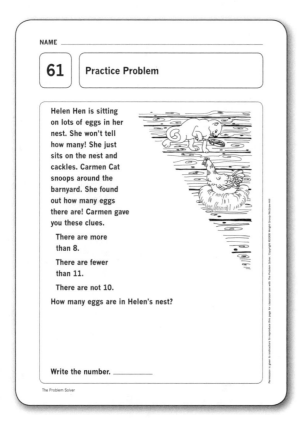

There are more than 8.

There are fewer than 11.

There are not 10.

How many eggs are in Helen's nest?

Write the number. _____

NAME

62 | Practice Problem

Minnie, Manny, Mo, and May Mouse went to the library to get their favorite books. Each of the mice got a book. Minnie's book is the largest. Manny's book does not have a picture on the cover. May is afraid of cats. She won't touch a book about cats! Which book did each mouse get from the library?

Draw a line from each mouse to the book he or she got.

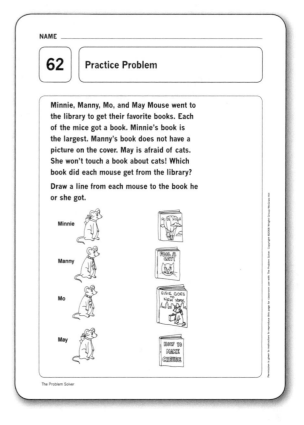

Minnie

Manny

Mo

May

You can find these pages on the CD

59 Problema para practicar

Uno de estos monos se llama Noodle.
Puedes hallar a Noodle si lo buscas bien.

Es el que está colgado patas arriba.

Es el que lleva puesto algo en la cabeza.

Es el que tiene una camisa a rayas.

¿Cuál de los monos es Noodle?

Pon un círculo alrededor de Noodle.

The Problem Solver

---

60 Problema para practicar

El señor y la señora Hippo quieren comprar
pintura y una nueva alfombra para la casa.
La tienda Hippo Home vende pintura azul
y amarilla. Vende alfombras verdes y
anaranjadas. El señor y la señora Hippo
pueden arreglar la casa con la nueva
pintura y la nueva alfombra. ¿Cuáles son
las 4 diferentes formas en que el señor y la
señora Hippo pueden arreglar su casa?

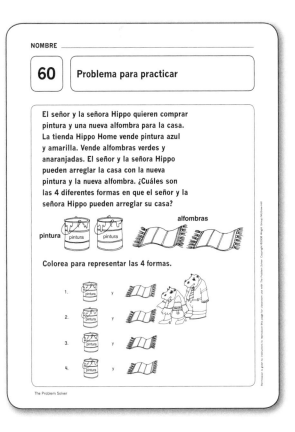

Colorea para representar las 4 formas.

1.
2.
3.
4.

The Problem Solver

---

61 Problema para practicar

Helen Hen está sentada
sobre un montón de huevos
en su nido. ¡Ella no quiere
decir cuantos huevos tiene!
Ella sólo se sienta sobre su
nido y cacarea. Carmen Cat
se desliza por el gallinero.
¡Carmen averiguó cuántos
huevos tiene Helen!
Carmen te da estas pistas.

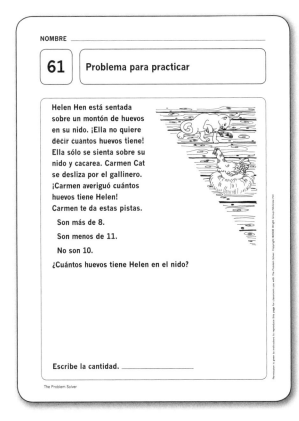

Son más de 8.

Son menos de 11.

No son 10.

¿Cuántos huevos tiene Helen en el nido?

Escribe la cantidad. _____

The Problem Solver

---

62 Problema para practicar

Minnie, Manny, Mo y May Mouse fueron a la
biblioteca para sacar sus libros favoritos.
El libro de Minnie es el más grande. El de
Manny no tiene un dibujo en la portada. May
le tiene miedo a los gatos. ¡Ella no toca un
libro acerca de los gatos! ¿Cuál libro sacó
cada ratoncito de la biblioteca?

Traza una línea desde cada ratoncito hasta el
libro que él o ella sacó.

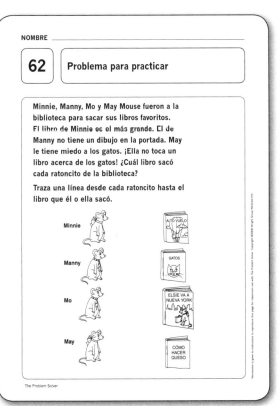

Minnie

Manny

Mo

May

ALTO VUELO

GATOS

ELSIE VA A NUEVA YORK

CÓMO HACER QUESO

The Problem Solver

You can find these pages on the CD

NAME

63 Practice Problem

Twinkle is going to the Earth's moon. Twinkle must pass 9 stars to get to the Earth's moon from his home moon. He starts out from his moon and flies past 5 stars. Whoosh! He lost his bag of moon dust! Twinkle turns around and flies past 3 stars. He finds his bag of moon dust. He turns around again and flies past 4 stars. Where is Twinkle now?

Write a *T* to show where Twinkle is.

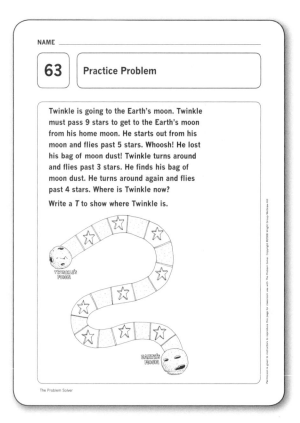

64 Practice Problem

Gail and her friend Sam make tasty lemon punch. They are going to buy 7 lemons to make more lemon punch. The store sells lemons in bags. What 3 different pairs of bags can Gail and Sam buy?

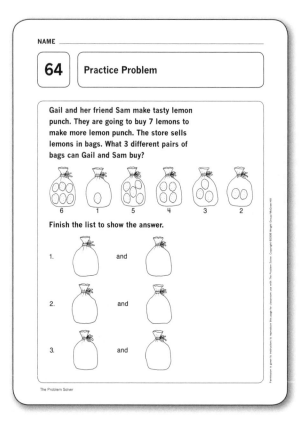

Finish the list to show the answer.

1. and
2. and
3. and

65 Practice Problem

Sandy, Lee, and Jerome counted their money. "We have 10 dollars in all," said Lee. "What can we buy?" The three children walked into a shop to look at the stuffed animals. Which 3 different animals can Sandy, Lee, and Jerome buy?

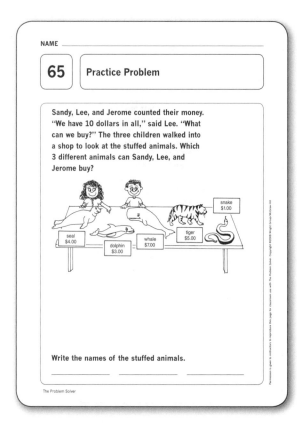

Write the names of the stuffed animals.

_____   _____   _____

66 Practice Problem

One day, Connie saw a trail of shells in the sand. There were snail shells, crab shells, and clam shells in the trail. Connie followed the trail until it went behind a big rock. Connie saw a pattern in the trail, so she knew which shell was behind the rock. Look for the pattern that Connie saw. What shell will Connie find behind the rock?

Draw the shell.

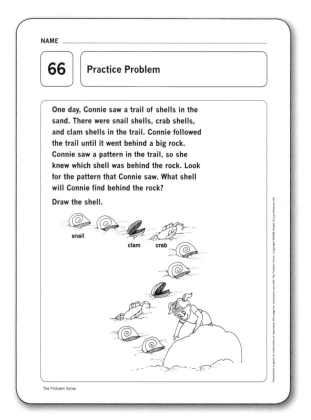

You can find these pages on the CD

NOMBRE

63 | Problema para practicar

Twinkle va a visitar la luna de la Tierra. Twinkle debe pasar por 9 estrellas para ir desde su luna hasta la luna de la Tierra. Él sale de su luna y pasa por 5 estrellas. ¡ZAS! ¡Twinkle perdió el polvo fugaz! Twinkle regresa y pasa por 3 estrellas. Él encuentra su bolsa con el polvo fugaz. Se da la vuelta y nuevamente pasa por 4 estrellas. ¿Dónde está Twinkle ahora?

Escribe una *T* para mostrar dónde está Twinkle.

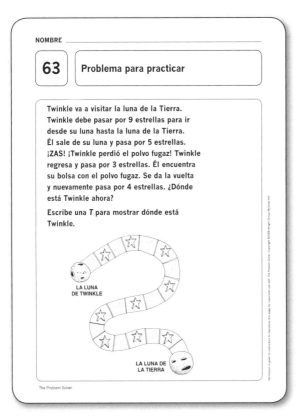

LA LUNA DE TWINKLE

LA LUNA DE LA TIERRA

The Problem Solver

NOMBRE

64 | Problema para practicar

Gail y su amigo Sam hacen una sabrosa limonada. Van a comprar 7 limones para hacer más limonada. La tienda vende los limones por bolsa. ¿Cuáles son los 3 pares de bolsas que Gail y Sam pueden comprar?

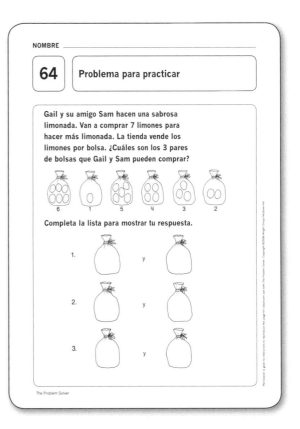

6   1   5   4   3   2

Completa la lista para mostrar tu respuesta.

1. _____ y _____

2. _____ y _____

3. _____ y _____

The Problem Solver

NOMBRE

65 | Problema para practicar

Sandy, Lee y Jerome contaron el dinero que tenían. "Tenemos 10 dólares en total", dijo Lee. "¿Qué podemos comprar?". Los tres niños caminaron hasta una tienda para ver los animales de juguete. ¿Cuáles son los 3 diferentes animales que Sandy, Lee y Jerome pueden comprar?

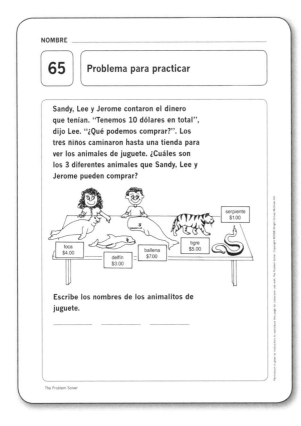

serpiente $1.00

foca $4.00

delfín $3.00

ballena $7.00

tigre $5.00

Escribe los nombres de los animalitos de juguete.

_____   _____   _____

The Problem Solver

NOMBRE

66 | Problema para practicar

Un día, Connie vio un camino en la arena hecho con caparazones de caracol, de cangrejo y de almejas. Connie siguió el camino hasta que llegó a una gran roca. Connie vio que había un patrón. Por eso ella sabía cuál era el caparazón de mar que estaba detrás de la roca. Busca el patrón que Connie vio. ¿Cuál es la concha de mar que Connie encuentra detrás de la roca?

Dibuja una concha de mar.

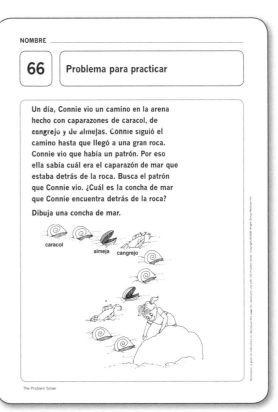

caracol   almeja   cangrejo

The Problem Solver

You can find these pages on the CD

67 Practice Problem

The Tintown Zoo has 5 elephants. One day they all walked to the water fountain, one after the other. Ben was first in line. Rita was in front of Molly. Amy was in front of Rita. Toby walked behind Molly. Where was each elephant in line?

Write each elephant's name next to it.

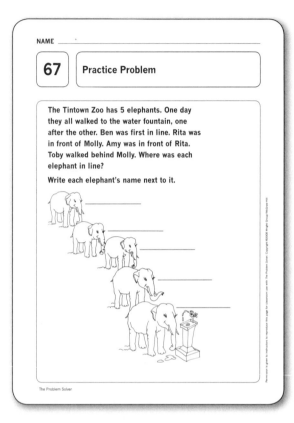

68 Practice Problem

Sam and Robyn Rabbit made a big salad for dinner. They peeled carrots and onions for the salad. Robyn peeled the onions. Sam peeled the carrots. Lucky Sam! Poor Robyn! She had to go dry her tears a lot. In the time it took Robyn to peel 1 onion, Sam peeled 3 carrots. They kept peeling onions and carrots in the same way until the salad was ready. Robyn peeled 5 onions in all. How many carrots did Sam peel?

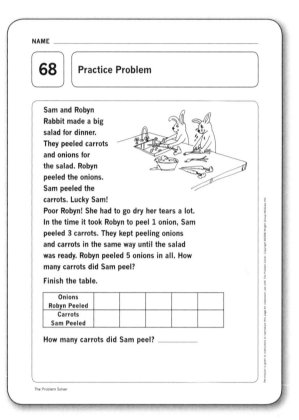

Finish the table.

Onions Robyn Peeled				
Carrots Sam Peeled				

How many carrots did Sam peel? _____

69 Practice Problem

Polly Porcupine hurried to her mailbox. She opened the box and saw 1 card. The next day Polly found 4 cards in her mailbox. On the third day she got 7 cards. Polly could see that every day she got 3 more cards than the day before. The cards on the fourth and fifth days followed that number pattern, too. How many cards did Polly get on the fifth day?

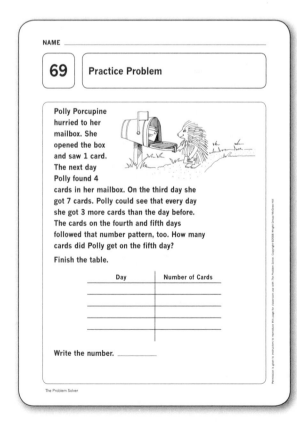

Finish the table.

Day	Number of Cards

Write the number.

70 Practice Problem

Mrs. Whozit's class is going on a field trip. There are 15 students in the class. They are riding in 3 vans. There are 11 students in all riding in van A and van B. There are 9 students in all riding in van B and van C. How many students are riding in each van?

Put counters on the vans to show the students.

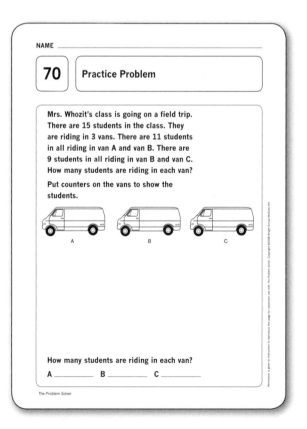

How many students are riding in each van?

A _____ B _____ C _____

You can find these pages on the CD

NOMBRE _____

67 | Problema para practicar

El Tintown Zoo tiene 5 elefantes. Un día, todos los elefantes caminaron hasta la fuente de agua, uno detrás del otro. Ben era el primero en la fila. Rita caminaba delante a Molly. Amy delante de Rita. Toby caminaba detrás de Molly. ¿En qué lugar de la fila está cada elefante?

Escribe el nombre de cada elefante.

The Problem Solver

NOMBRE _____

68 | Problema para practicar

Sam y Robyn Rabbit hicieron una rica ensalada para la cena. Ellos pelaron las zanahorias y las cebollas para ponerlas en la ensalada. Robyn peló las cebollas. Sam peló las zanahorias. ¡Qué suerte, Sam! ¡Pobre Robyn! Robyn tuvo que ir a secarse las lágrimas muchas veces. En el tiempo que le tomó a Robyn pelar 1 cebolla, Sam peló 3 zanahorias. Ellos continuaron pelando cebollas y zanahorias de la misma manera hasta que terminaron de hacer la ensalada. Robyn peló 5 cebollas en total.

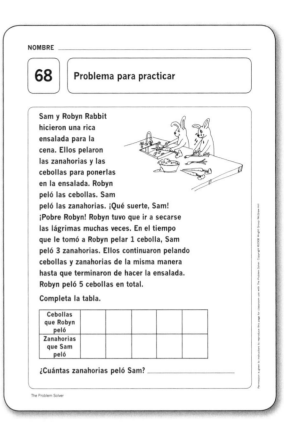

Completa la tabla.

Cebollas que Robyn peló					
Zanahorias que Sam peló					

¿Cuántas zanahorias peló Sam? _____

The Problem Solver

NOMBRE _____

69 | Problema para practicar

Polly Porcupine corre a abrir su buzón y saca 1 tarjeta. El siguiente día, Polly recibe 4 tarjetas. El tercer día ella recibe 7 tarjetas. Ella se da cuenta de que cada día recibe 3 tarjetas más que las del día anterior. Las tarjetas que recibe el cuarto y el quinto día tienen el mismo patrón numérico. ¿Cuántas tarjetas recibe Polly el quinto día?

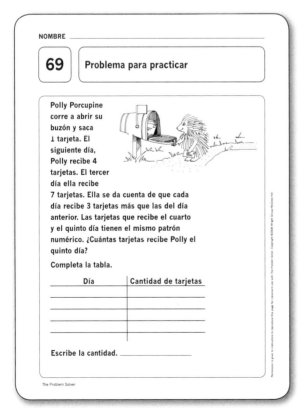

Completa la tabla.

Día	Cantidad de tarjetas

Escribe la cantidad. _____

The Problem Solver

NOMBRE _____

70 | Problema para practicar

La clase de la señora Whozit va a dar un paseo por el campo. Hay 15 estudiantes en la clase. Ellos van a ir en 3 camionetas. Van 15 estudiantes en las camionetas A y B. Van 9 estudiantes en las camionetas B y C. ¿Cuántos estudiantes en total van en cada camioneta?

Pon las fichas en las camionetas para mostrar los estudiantes.

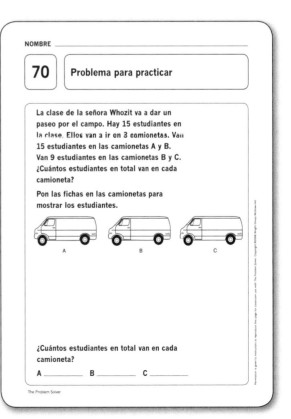

¿Cuántos estudiantes en total van en cada camioneta?

A _____ B _____ C _____

The Problem Solver

You can find these pages on the CD

NAME _____

71 | Practice Problem

Blinker Bear sells honey to other bears. The bears pay 5 cents if they buy 1 pail of honey. If they buy more honey, they pay 2 cents for each pail after the first one. Today Blinker sold 6 pails of honey to Brice Bear. How much money did Brice pay for the honey?

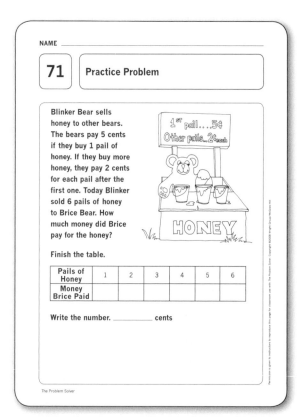

Finish the table.

Pails of Honey	1	2	3	4	5	6
Money Brice Paid						

Write the number. _____ cents

The Problem Solver

NAME _____

72 | Practice Problem

Don't let Billy Bighorn into your flower garden! He eats flowers. He ate 8 flowers in Alice's garden. He ate 10 flowers in Bonnie's garden and 12 flowers in Corbin's garden. Then he swallowed 14 flowers from Don's garden. It looks like Billy was following a number pattern and getting hungrier! How many flowers did Billy swallow in the next garden?

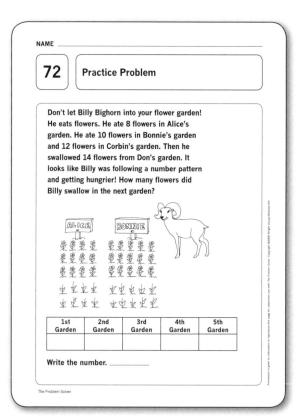

1st Garden	2nd Garden	3rd Garden	4th Garden	5th Garden

Write the number. _____

The Problem Solver

NAME _____

73 | Practice Problem

Mitra, Joan, and Ariel are sisters. Mitra is the oldest. She is 5 years older than Joan. Joan has not been going to school very long. She is only 2 years older than Ariel. Ariel is 4 years old. She is the youngest of the girls. How old is Mitra?

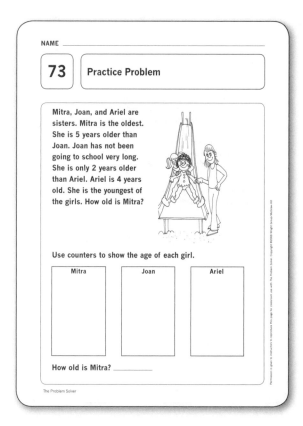

Use counters to show the age of each girl.

Mitra	Joan	Ariel

How old is Mitra? _____

The Problem Solver

NAME _____

74 | Practice Problem

Debby Duck lives in a lake. She swims from her lake to the river to look for fish. There are 2 little streams from her lake to a pond. There are 3 big streams from the pond to the river. Debby likes to take a different path to the river every day. What are all the different paths Debby can take from her lake to the river?

Use a different color to trace each path.

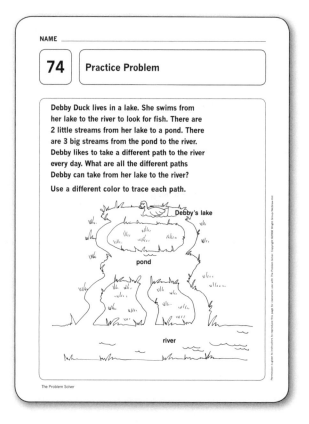

The Problem Solver

You can find these pages on the CD

71 Problema para practicar

Blinker Bear le vende miel a los otros osos. Los osos pagan 5¢ si compran 1 balde de miel. Si compran más miel, pagan 2¢ por cada balde después del primero. Hoy Blinker vendió 6 baldes de miel a Brice Bear. ¿Cuánto dinero pagó Brice por la miel?

1 balde . . . . 5¢
Baldes adicionales . . . 2¢ cada uno

Completa la tabla.

Balde de miel	1	2	3	4	5	6
Dinero que pagó Brice						

Escribe el número. _____ centavos

72 Problema para practicar

¡No dejes que Billy Bighorn entre en tu jardín! Él se come las flores. Se comió 8 flores del jardín de Alice. Se comió 10 flores del jardín de Bonnie y 12 del jardín de Corbin. Después se comió 14 flores del jardín de Don. Parece que Billy se come las flores siguiendo un patrón numérico, ¡y tiene más hambre! ¿Cuántas flores del siguiente jardín se comerá Billy?

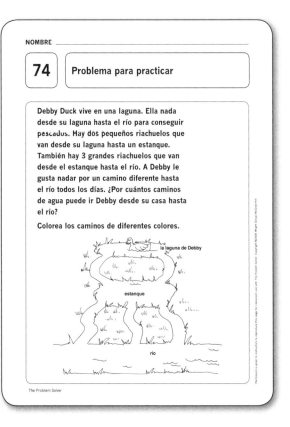

Jardín 1	Jardín 2	Jardín 3	Jardín 4	Jardín 5

Escribe el número. _____

73 Problema para practicar

Mitra, Joan y Ariel son hermanas. Mitra es la mayor. Ella es 5 años mayor que Joan. No hace mucho tiempo, Joan empezó a asistir a la escuela. Ella es 2 años mayor que Ariel. Ariel tiene 4 años de edad. Ella es la menor de las hermanas. ¿Cuántos años tiene Mitra?

Usa las fichas para representar la edad de cada niña.

Mitra	Joan	Ariel

¿Cuántos años tiene Mitra? _____

74 Problema para practicar

Debby Duck vive en una laguna. Ella nada desde su laguna hasta el río para conseguir pescados. Hay dos pequeños riachuelos que van desde su laguna hasta un estanque. También hay 3 grandes riachuelos que van desde el estanque hasta el río. A Debby le gusta nadar por un camino diferente hasta el río todos los días. ¿Por cuántos caminos de agua puede ir Debby desde su casa hasta el río?

Colorea los caminos de diferentes colores.

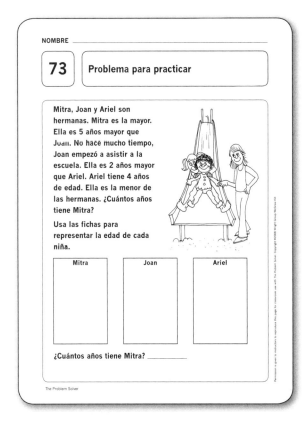

You can find these pages on the CD

75 | Practice Problem

Maya made a board for a game. She drew 5 dots on paper. Then she and Laura began to play the game. They drew lines from dot to dot. Laura won! When they finished playing the game, there was a line drawn from each dot to every other dot on the board. How many lines were drawn on the board?

Show your work.

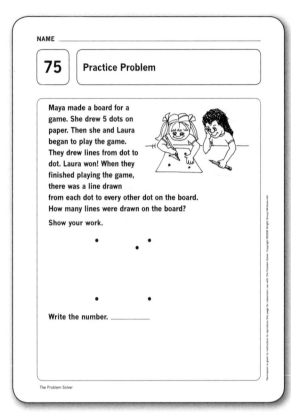

Write the number. _____

The Problem Solver

76 | Practice Problem

Sasha is giving you a puzzle to solve. She says, "There are a star and an oval on the floor. There are 5 elephants standing in the star. There are 3 elephants standing in the oval. But there are only 5 elephants in all. Where is the oval, and where are the elephants?"

Draw the oval.

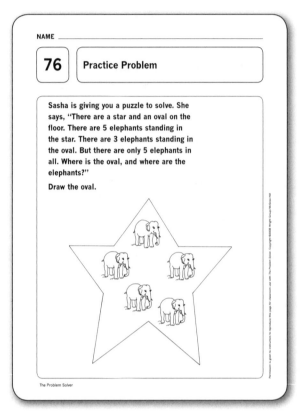

The Problem Solver

77 | Practice Problem

In Mr. D.'s class, the children sign up for jobs. The graph shows how many children signed up for each end-of-the-day job.

- Rob's job has three people.
- Amber's job and washing tables have equal numbers of workers.
- Liz's job has only half as many workers as putting up chairs.

Which jobs do Rob, Amber, and Liz have?

Use the graph and the clues.

End-of-the-Day Jobs

Put Away Materials	X	X	X	X	X	X					
Put Up Chairs	X	X	X	X							
Erase Boards	X	X	X								
Sweep	X	X									
Wash Tables	X	X	X	X	X	X					

How Many Workers

Rob _____

Amber _____

Liz _____

The Problem Solver

78 | Practice Problem

Mrs. Day's class has been keeping track of the high temperatures each day this week. The graph shows the highest temperature reached on each day. Different children like different temperatures.

- Nick liked the coolest temperature.
- Sam liked the temperature on the day that was 5 degrees warmer than Monday.
- Emma liked the temperature on the days that were 10 degrees cooler than Friday.

Which days did Nick, Sam, and Emma like?

Use the graph and the clues.

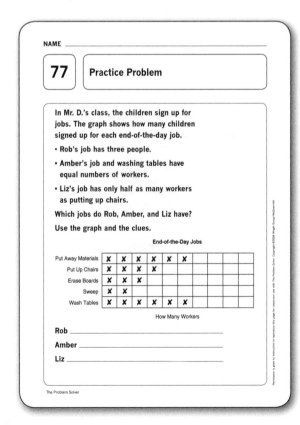

This Week's Temperatures

Nick liked _____

Sam liked _____

Emma liked _____ and _____

The Problem Solver

You can find these pages on the CD

75 Problema para practicar

Maya hizo un tablero para un
juego. Dibujó cinco puntos
en un papel. Después ella
y Laura empezaron a jugar.
Ellas trazaron líneas de un
punto al otro. ¡Laura ganó!
Cuando terminaron de jugar,
había una línea entre todos los puntos en el
tablero. ¿Cuántas líneas tiene el tablero?

Muestra tu trabajo.

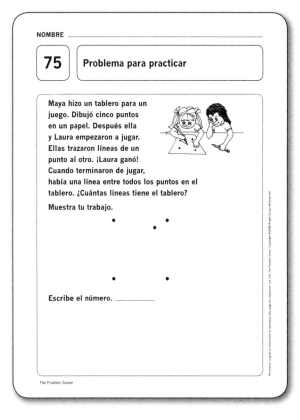

Escribe el número. _____

76 Problema para practicar

Sasha te da una adivinanza para que la
resuelvas. "En el piso están dibujados
una estrella y un óvalo. 5 elefantes están
parados sobre la estrella. 3 elefantes están
parados sobre el óvalo. Pero solamente hay
5 elefantes en total. ¿Dónde está el óvalo y
dónde están los elefantes?

Dibuja el óvalo.

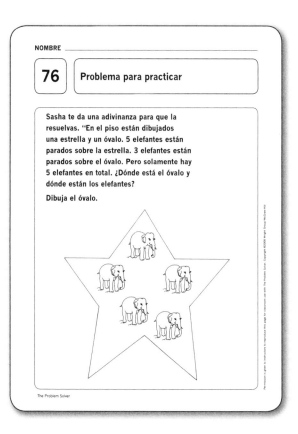

77 Problema para practicar

En la clase del señor D. los niños se anotan
para hacer trabajos al final del día. La
gráfica muestra cuántos niños se anotaron.

• El trabajo que hace Rob tiene 3 personas.

• El trabajo que hace Amber, y el de
limpiar las mesas, tiene igual cantidad de
personas.

• El trabajo que hace Liz tiene sólo la mitad
de las personas que ponen las sillas.

¿Cuáles son los trabajos que hacen Rob,
Amber y Liz?

Usa la gráfica y las pistas.

Trabajos para hacer al final del día

Guardar los materiales	X	X	X	X	X	X	
Poner las sillas	X	X	X	X			
Borrar el pizarrón	X	X	X				
Barrer	X	X					
Limpiar las mesas	X	X	X	X	X	X	

Cantidad de niños

Rob _____

Amber _____

Liz _____

78 Problema para practicar

La clase de la señora Day llevó la cuenta
de las temperaturas diarias durante una
semana. La gráfica muestra la temperatura
más alta de cada día. No a todos los niños
les gusta la misma temperatura.

• A Nick le gusta cuando la temperatura está
baja y hace frío.

• A Sam le gusta la temperatura del día que
estaba a 5 grados más caliente que el lunes.

• A Emma le gusta la temperatura del día que
estaba a 10 grados más frío que el viernes.

¿Qué días les gustan a Nick, Sam y Emma?
Usa la gráfica y las pistas.

Las temperaturas de la semana

85°
80°
75°
70°
65°
60°

Lunes   Martes   Miércoles   Jueves   Viernes

A Nick le gusta _____.

A Sam le gusta _____.

A Emma le gustan _____ y _____.

You can find these pages on the CD

NAME

79 Practice Problem

Carly hid some special polished rocks around the yard for her friends to find. Carly didn't tell her friends how many rocks she hid. She just gave them some clues.

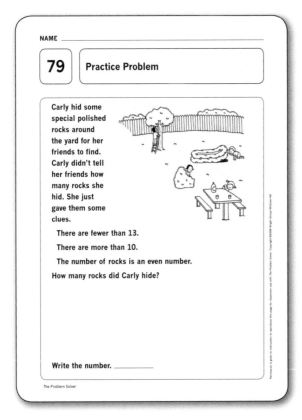

There are fewer than 13.

There are more than 10.

The number of rocks is an even number.

How many rocks did Carly hide?

Write the number. _____

The Problem Solver

NAME

80 Practice Problem

Jenna and Maddy went to the school carnival. At one booth, there's a math game. If Jenna and Maddy can pick 2 coin purses with a total of 11 coins in them all together, they will win a prize. Which 5 different pairs of coin purses could Jenna and Maddy choose?

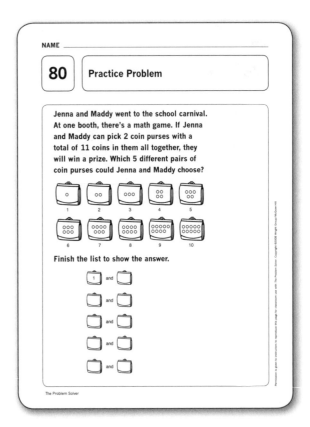

Finish the list to show the answer.

1 and ☐

☐ and ☐

☐ and ☐

☐ and ☐

☐ and ☐

The Problem Solver

NAME

81 Practice Problem

Thea raced to the snack booth at the school fun fair. She had 18 tickets to spend. She bought 3 snacks and used all her tickets. Which 3 snacks did she get?

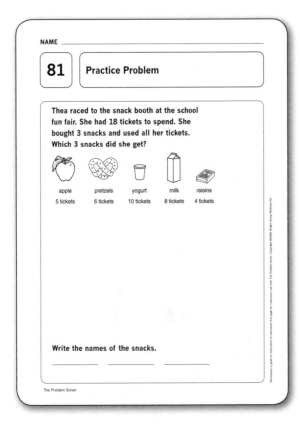

| apple | pretzels | yogurt | milk | raisins |
| 5 tickets | 6 tickets | 10 tickets | 8 tickets | 4 tickets |

Write the names of the snacks.

_____ _____ _____

The Problem Solver

NAME

82 Practice Problem

Lucy loves wearing rings on her fingers. She is always careful to put them away when she goes to bed. She has 14 rings that she keeps in 3 jewelry boxes. There are 10 rings in all in box A and box B. There are 7 rings in all in box B and box C. How many rings are in each box?

Put counters on the jewelry boxes to show the rings.

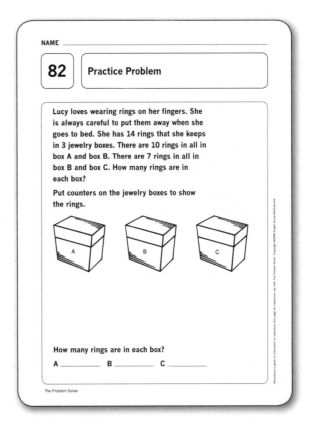

How many rings are in each box?

A _____ B _____ C _____

The Problem Solver

---

128   The Problem Solver

You can find these pages on the CD

79 | Problema para practicar

Carly escondió unas rocas especiales por su patio para que sus amigos las buscaran. Carly no les dijo a sus amigos cuántas rocas escondió. Ella solamente les dio algunas pistas.

Son menos de 13.

Son más de 10.

La cantidad es un número par.

¿Cuántas rocas escondió Carly?

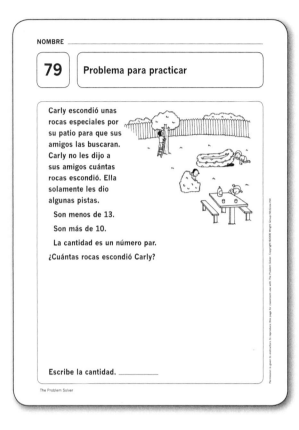

Escribe la cantidad. _____

The Problem Solver

80 | Problema para practicar

Jenna y Maddy van al carnaval de la escuela. En una caseta hay un juego de matemáticas. Si Jenna y Maddy pueden elegir 2 monederos que entre los dos tengan un total de 11 centavos, ellas ganan un premio. ¿Cuáles son los diferentes pares de monederos que Jenna 5 Maddy pueden elegir?

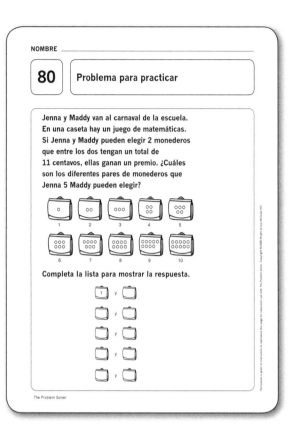

Completa la lista para mostrar la respuesta.

The Problem Solver

81 | Problema para practicar

Thea corrió hacia la caseta de las meriendas en la feria de la escuela. Ella tenía 18 boletos para gastar. Compró 3 meriendas y usó todos sus boletos. ¿Cuáles son las meriendas que compró Thea?

| manzana | pretzels | yogur | leche | uvas pasas |
| 5 boletos | 6 boletos | 10 boletos | 8 boletos | 4 boletos |

Escribe los nombres de las meriendas.

_____ _____ _____

The Problem Solver

82 | Problema para practicar

A Lucy le encanta usar anillos en sus dedos. Ella es cuidadosa y se los quita antes de acostarse. Lucy tiene 14 anillos y los guarda en 3 joyeros. Ella guarda un total de 10 anillos en los joyeros A y B. Guarda un total de 7 anillos en los joyeros B y C. ¿Cuántos anillos guarda en cada joyero?

Pon las fichas en los joyeros para mostrar los anillos.

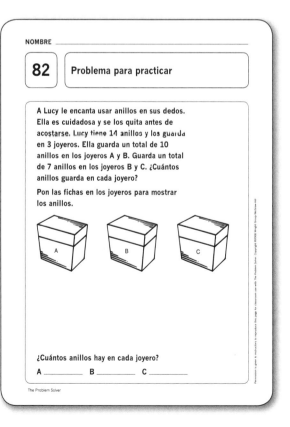

¿Cuántos anillos hay en cada joyero?

A _____ B _____ C _____

The Problem Solver

Answer Key

Teaching Problem/Solution

1

1

2

hexagon

2

hexágono

3

race car

van

fire truck

lumber truck

motorcycle

3

camioneta

Teaching Problem/Solution

4 Red sneakers and blue socks

red sneakers and green socks

yellow sneakers and blue socks

yellow sneakers and green socks

5 Striped mittens and red cap

striped mittens and blue cap

diamond design mittens and red cap

diamond design mittens and blue cap

6 Apple and peanut butter

apple and cheese

onion and peanut butter

onion and cheese

7 7 goldfish

8 9 kittens

9 11 bones

10

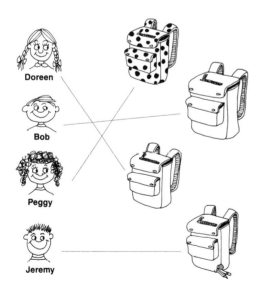

4 Zapatos rojos y calcetines azules

zapatos rojos y calcetines verdes

zapatos amarillos y calcetines azules

zapatos amarillos y calcetines verdes

5 Mitones a rayas y una gorra roja

mitones a rayas y una gorra azul

mitones con diseño de diamante y una gorra roja

mitones con diseño de diamante y una gorra azul

6 Manzana y mantequilla de maní

manzana y queso

cebolla y mantequilla de maní

cebolla y queso

7 7 peces

8 9 gatitos

9 11 huesos

10

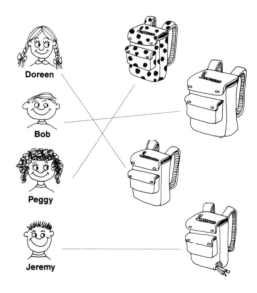

Teaching Problem/Solution

11

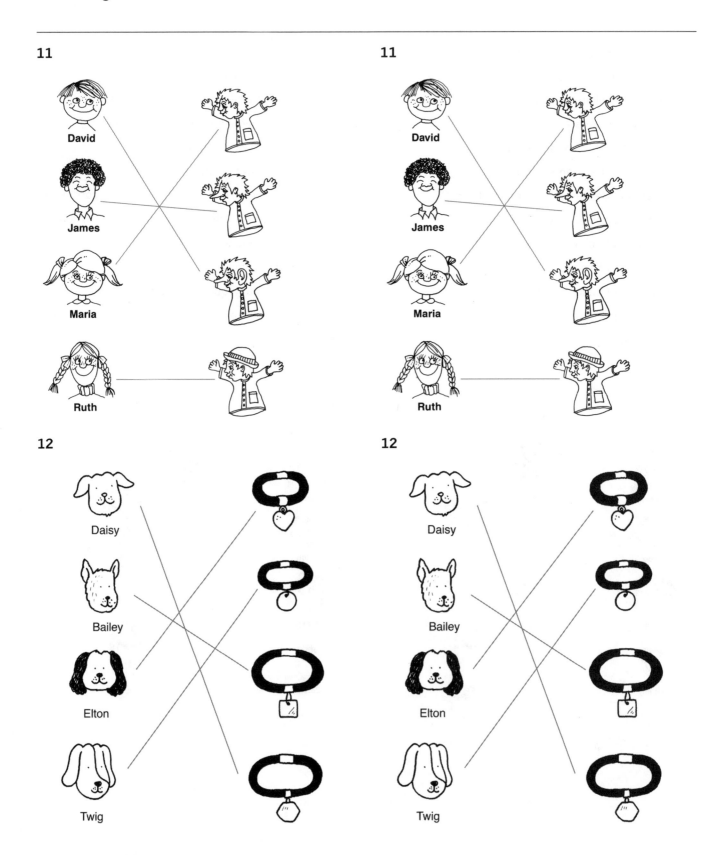

11

David

James

Maria

Ruth

12

Daisy

Bailey

Elton

Twig

12

Daisy

Bailey

Elton

Twig

Teaching Problem/Solution

13

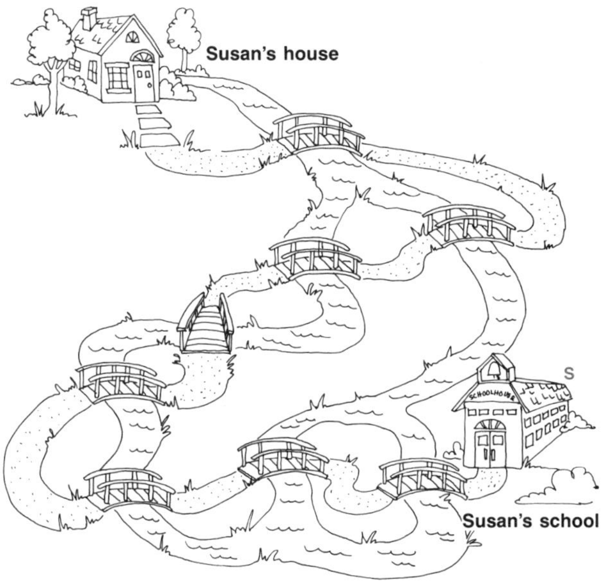

Susan's house

S

Susan's school

13

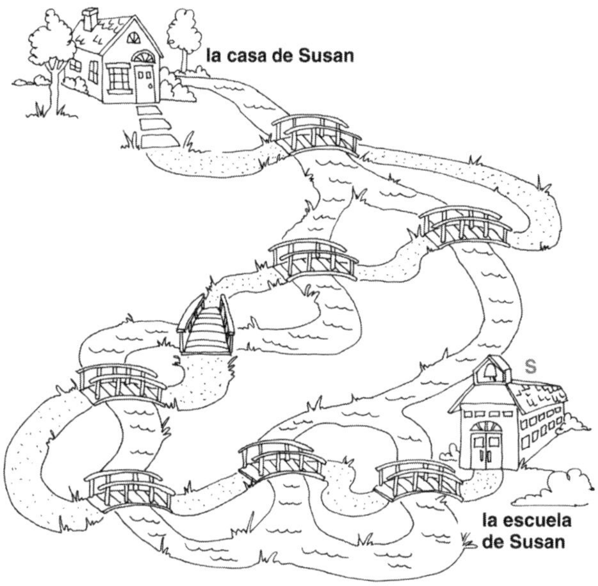

la casa de Susan

S

la escuela de Susan

14

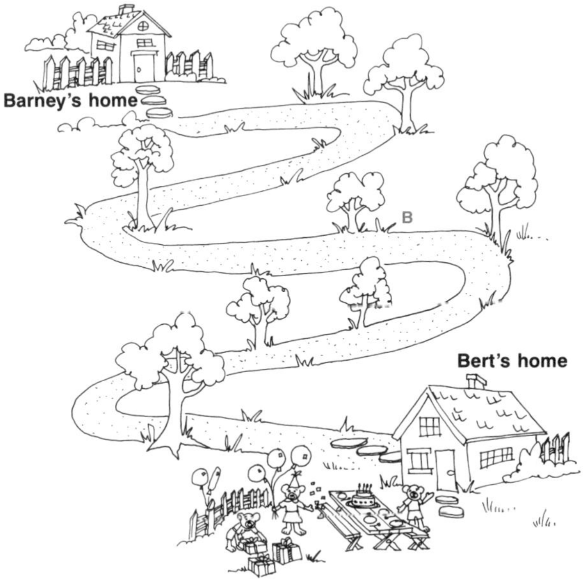

Barney's home

B

Bert's home

14

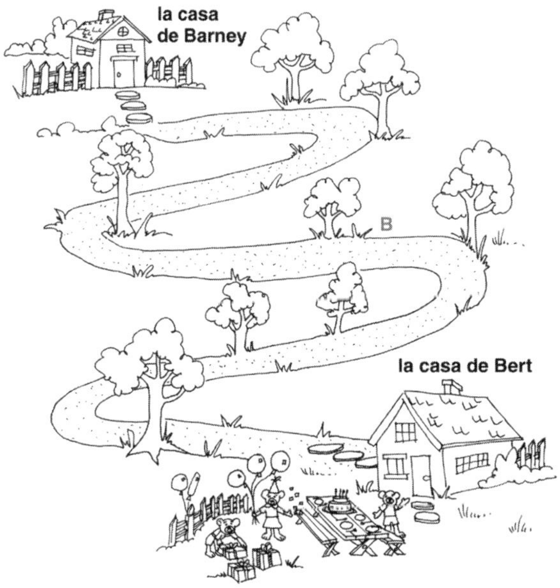

la casa de Barney

B

la casa de Bert

Teaching Problem/Solution

15

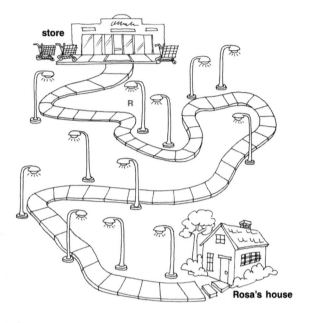

store

R

Rosa's house

15

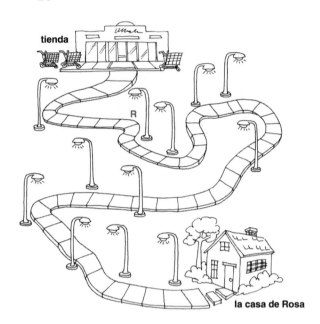

tienda

R

la casa de Rosa

16

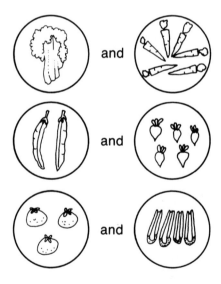

and

and

and

16

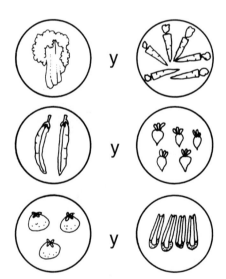

y

y

y

Teaching Problem/Solution

17

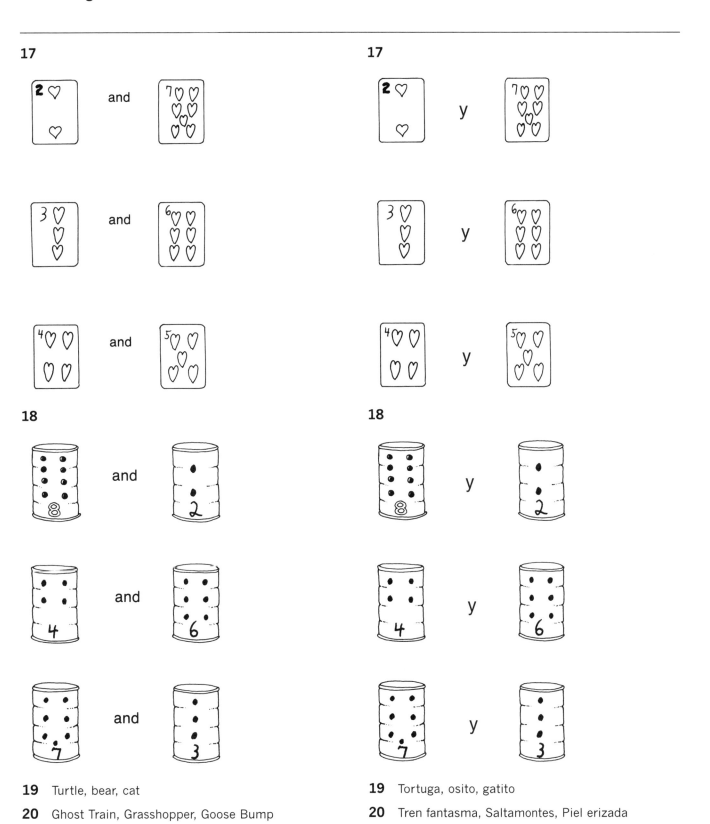

2 ♡ ♡   and   7 ♡ ♡ ♡ ♡ ♡ ♡ ♡

3 ♡ ♡ ♡   and   6 ♡ ♡ ♡ ♡ ♡ ♡

4 ♡ ♡ ♡ ♡   and   5 ♡ ♡ ♡ ♡ ♡

18

8   and   2

4   and   6

7   and   3

19 Turtle, bear, cat

20 Ghost Train, Grasshopper, Goose Bump

17

2 ♡ ♡   y   7 ♡ ♡ ♡ ♡ ♡ ♡ ♡

3 ♡ ♡ ♡   y   6 ♡ ♡ ♡ ♡ ♡ ♡

4 ♡ ♡ ♡ ♡   y   5 ♡ ♡ ♡ ♡ ♡

18

8   y   2

4   y   6

7   y   3

19 Tortuga, osito, gatito

20 Tren fantasma, Saltamontes, Piel erizada

Teaching Problem/Solution

21 Walk the dog, wash the car, put out garbage; or rake, water flowers, and put out garbage

21 Sacar al perro, lavar el carro, sacar la basura, o barrer las hojas, regar las Plantas, sacar la basura

22

22

23 Owl

23 Búho

24

 red

24

 roja

25 Yellow

25 Amarillo

26 Tom

26 Tom

27

27

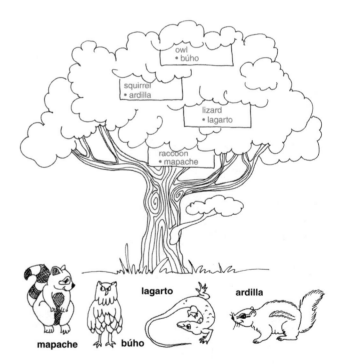

28 12 notes

28 12 invitaciones

29 16 crumbs

29 16 migajas

30 14 balloons

30 14 globos

31 12 blocks

31 12 bloques

32 20 plums

32 20 ciruelas

Teaching Problem/Solution

33	18 stones
34	Table A—1 pet, Table B—4 pets, Table C—3 pets
35	Plate A—4 mud pies, plate B—2 mud pies, plate C—6 mud pies
36	Log A—5 frogs, log B—4 frogs, log C—2 frogs
37	14 wheels
38	12 cents
39	16 pigs
40	9 nuts
41	12 tadpoles
42	4 people
43	11 fish
44	13 berries
45	15 cards
46	

33	18 rocas
34	Mesa A—1 mascota, Mesa B—4 mascotas, Mesa C—3 mascotas
35	Plato A—4 pasteles de barro, Plato B—2 pasteles de barro, Plato C—6 pasteles de barro
36	Tronco A—5 sapitos, Tronco B—4 sapitos, Tronco C—2 sapitos
37	14 ruedas
38	12 centavos
39	16 cerditos
40	9 nueces
41	12 renacuajos
42	4 personas
43	11 pescados
44	13 bayas
45	15 tarjetas
46	

Teaching Problem/Solution

47

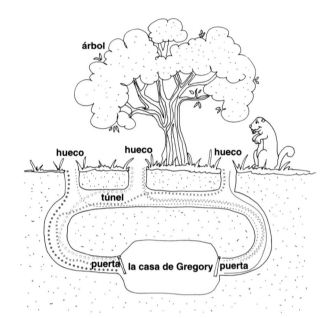

47

48

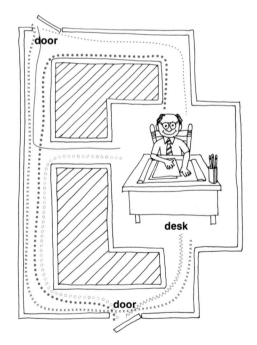

48

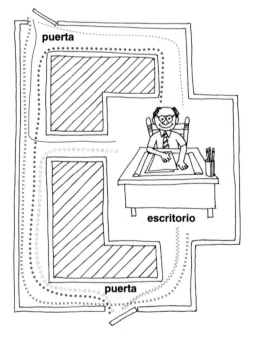

49 6 ribbons

50 6 hand slaps

51 10 games

49 6 cintas

50 6 veces chocan las manos

51 10 partidos

Teaching Problem/Solution

52

52

53

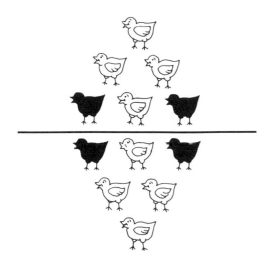

53

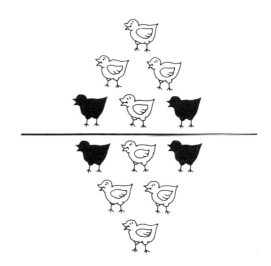

54 3 snails

55 Sean—kickball, Rachel—tag,
Alyssa—jump rope

56 Isabelle—bus, Julian—walk,
Lauren—car

57 Oscar—3 cats, Ali—4 birds, Asia—8 fish

58 Marta's—4 inches, Alex's—6 inches,
Nia's—10 inches

54 3 caracoles

55 Sean—patear la pelota, Rachel—correr,
Alyssa—saltar la cuerda

56 Isabelle—autobús, Julian—caminando,
Lauren—carro

57 Oscar—3 gatos, Ali—4 aves, Asia—8 peces

58 El de Marta—4 pulgadas, el de Alex—6 pulgadas,
el de Nía—10 pulgadas

Practice Problem/Solution

Note: The strategies shown for the Practice Problems are those which were used for solving the similar Teaching Problems. However, students' choices of strategy may vary.

59

59

60

Paint **blue**	and	 **green**
 Paint **blue**	and	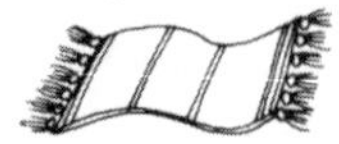 **orange**
 Paint **yellow**	and	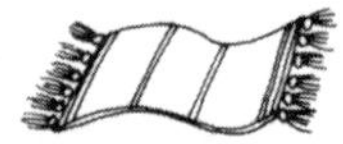 **green**
 Paint **yellow**	and	 **orange**

60

Pintura **azul**	y	 **verde**
 Pintura **azul**	y	 **anaranjada**
 Pintura **amarilla**	y	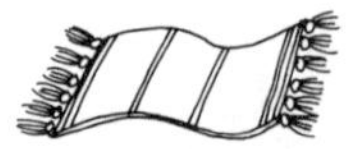 **verde**
 Pintura **amarilla**	y	 **anaranjada**

Practice Problem/Solution

Note: The strategies shown for the Practice Problems are those which were used for solving the similar Teaching Problems. However, students' choices of strategy may vary.

61 9

1. 0
2. 00
3. 000
4. 0000
5. 00000
6. 000000
7. 0000000
8. 00000000
9. 000000000
10. 0000000000
11. 00000000000

61 9

1. 0
2. 00
3. 000
4. 0000
5. 00000
6. 000000
7. 0000000
8. 00000000
9. 000000000
10. 0000000000
11. 00000000000

62

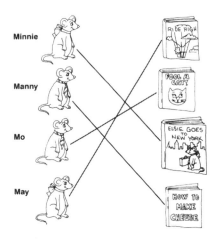

62

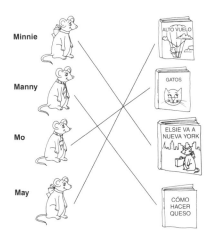

Practice Problem/Solution

Note: The strategies shown for the Practice Problems are those which were used for solving the similar Teaching Problems. However, students' choices of strategy may vary.

63

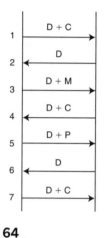

63

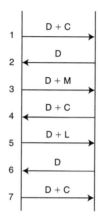

64

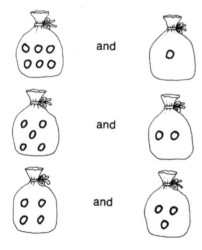

64

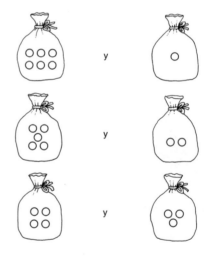

65 Tiger, seal, snake

66 Clam

65 Tigre, foca, serpiente

66 Concha de mar

Practice Problem/Solution

Note: The strategies shown for the Practice Problems are those which were used for solving the similar Teaching Problems. However, students' choices of strategy may vary.

67

68 15

Onions Robyn Peeled	1	2	3	4	5
Carrots Sam Peeled	3	6	9	12	15

69 13

Day	Number of Cards
1st	1
2nd	4
3rd	7
4th	10
5th	13

70 Van A—6 students, Van B—5 students, Van C—4 students

71 15¢

Pails of Honey	1	2	3	4	5	6
Money Brice Paid	5¢	7¢	9¢	11¢	13¢	15¢

72 16

1st Garden	2nd Garden	3rd Garden	4th Garden	5th Garden
8	10	12	14	16

67

68 15

Cebollas que Robyn peló	1	2	3	4	5
Zanahorias que Sam peló	3	6	9	12	15

69 13

Día	Cantidad de tarjetas
1st	1
2nd	4
3rd	7
4th	10
5th	13

70 Camioneta A—6 estudiantes, Camioneta B—5 estudiantes, Camioneta C—4 estudiantes

71 15¢

Baldes de miel	1	2	3	4	5	6
Dinero que pagó Brice	5¢	7¢	9¢	11¢	13¢	15¢

72 16

Jardín 1	Jardín 2	Jardín 3	Jardín 4	Jardín 5
8	10	12	14	16

Practice Problem/Solution

Note: The strategies shown for the Practice Problems are those which were used for solving the similar Teaching Problems. However, students' choices of strategy may vary.

---

73 11

Ariel = 4

Joan = 4 + 2 = 6

Mitra = 6 + 5 = 11

74

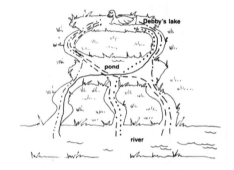

75 10

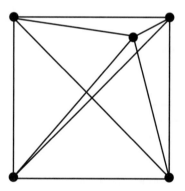

2 dots—1 line

3 dots—3 lines

4 dots—6 lines

5 dots—10 lines

73 11

Ariel = 4

Joan = 4 + 2 = 6

Mitra = 6 + 5 = 11

74

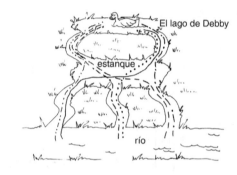

75 10

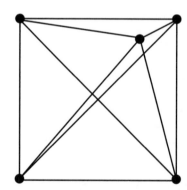

2 puntos—1 línea

3 puntos—3 líneas

4 puntos—6 líneas

5 puntos—10 líneas

Practice Problem/Solution

Note: The strategies shown for the Practice Problems are those which were used for solving the similar Teaching Problems. However, students' choices of strategy may vary.

76

76

77 Rob—erase boards, Amber—put away materials, Liz—sweep

78 Nick—Tuesday, Sam—Friday, Emma—Wednesday and Thursday

79 12

~~1. 0~~
~~2. 00~~
~~3. 000~~
~~4. 0000~~
~~5. 00000~~
~~6. 000000~~
~~7. 0000000~~
~~8. 00000000~~
~~9. 000000000~~
~~10. 0000000000~~
~~11. 00000000000~~
 12. 000000000000
~~13. 0000000000000~~

77 Rob—borrar pizarrones, Amber—guardar los materiales, Liz—barrer

78 Nick—martes, Sam—viernes, Emma—miércoles y jueves

79 12

~~1. 0~~
~~2. 00~~
~~3. 000~~
~~4. 0000~~
~~5. 00000~~
~~6. 000000~~
~~7. 0000000~~
~~8. 00000000~~
~~9. 000000000~~
~~10. 0000000000~~
~~11. 00000000000~~
 12. 000000000000
~~13. 0000000000000~~

Practice Problem/Solution

Note: The strategies shown for the Practice Problems are those which were used for solving the similar Teaching Problems. However, students' choices of strategy may vary.

80

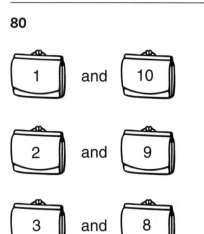 and

 and

and

 and

and

81 Pretzels, milk, raisins

$6 + 8 + 4 = 18$

82 Box A—7 rings, Box B—3 rings, Box C—4 rings

80

 y

 y

 y

 y

 y

81 Pretzels, leche, uvas pasas

$6 + 8 + 4 = 18$

82 Caja A—7 anillos, Caja B—3 anillos, Caja C—4 anillos